Fossil Collecting

FOSSIL COLLECTING:
An Illustrated Guide

by

RICHARD CASANOVA

edited by

Vinson Brown

English edition prepared by

Elaine Bryant

FABER AND FABER

London

First published in 1960
by Faber and Faber Limited
24 Russell Square London W.C.1
First published in this edition 1970
Printed in Great Britain by
Latimer Trend & Co Ltd Plymouth
All rights reserved

© Richard Casanova
1960

SBN (paper edition) 571 09470 8
SBN (cloth edition) 571 06093 5

Acknowledgements

In producing this English edition, I should like to thank Vinson Brown and Richard Casanova for their interest and help, and the Rochester Museum of Arts and Science for permission to reproduce plates 33, 34, 35 and 36. Of my former colleagues at Imperial College, London, Miss P. Yates and Mr. J. Gee have given advice and assistance in the preparation of plates, Dr. D. V. Ager edited the fossil plant section, and Dr. M. Kerney gave valuable assistance by reading and criticising the manuscript.

I am also indebted to the British Museum (Natural History) for permission to reproduce plates 14, 15, 28, 29, 30 and 31, and to Dr. J. C. Harper of the Geology Department, Liverpool University, for making available the specimens shown in plates 12, 23 and 27. Finally I am most grateful to the publishers for the help and encouragement they have given during the preparation of this book.

Contents

7

Illustrations

PLATES
after page 32

1. *Nummulites laevigatus*. A foraminifer from the Lower Bracklesham Beds, Eocene, Whitecliff Bay, Isle of Wight.
2. *Raphidonema faringdonense*. A vase-shaped calcareous sponge from the Cretaceous Faringdon Sponge Bed at Faringdon, Berkshire.
3. '*Omphyma*' *turbinata*. A large single coral from the Silurian Wenlock Limestone of Wenlock Edge.
4. *Lonsdaleia floriformis*. A compound rugose coral which is found quite commonly in the Carboniferous.
5. *Didymograptus murchisonae*. A tuning-fork graptolite from the Ordovician of Abereiddy Bay.
6. *Eschara pertusa*. An encrusting bryozoan from the Pliocene Coralline Crag at Sudbourne.
7. Silurian Wenlock Limestone with bryozoan colonies, crinoid ossicles, etc.
8. A typical decalcified shelly siltstone or sandstone of the Lower Palaeozoic, with brachiopods (*Orthis*, *Chonetes*), crinoid ossicles, etc.
9. *Epithyris bathonica*. A terebratulid from the Upper Jurassic rocks of Gloucestershire.
10. *Rhynchonella quadriplicata* from the Jurassic rocks of the Cotswolds.
11. *Asaphus cf. tyrannus*. A trilobite from the Ordovician rocks near Builth Wells.
12. *Trinucleus concentricus*. A specimen found in Ordovician rocks in Trilobite Dingle near Welshpool.

9

13. *Calymene blumenbachi*. A common trilobite of the Silurian Wenlock Limestone. This specimen was collected near Dudley.
14. *Heterophlebia buckmani*. A Liassic dragonfly from the Jurassic rocks of Gloucestershire.
15. A model of *Eurypterus*.
16. *Venericardia planicosta*. An Eocene lamellibranch from the Bracklesham Beds at Southampton; exterior and interior views.
17. *Aequipecten opercularis*. A Pliocene scallop from the Coralline Crag at Sudbourne Hall, Suffolk.
18. *Voluta spinosa*. A Lower Oligocene gastropod from the Isle of Wight.
19. *Asteroceras obtusum*. A Lower Lias ammonite from Lyme Regis, Dorset.

after page 64

20. *Euhoplites proboscideus*. A Gault (Cretaceous) ammonite from the Isle of Wight.
21. *Nautilus*. A specimen of Lower Cretaceous age.
22. *Gissocrinus goniodactylus*. A Silurian crinoid.
23. *Ophioderma carinata*. A fossil starfish from the Middle Lias of Yorkshire.
24. *Hemicidaris intermedia*. A Jurassic echinoid from the Coral Rag at Colne, Wiltshire. *Hemicidaris* is a regular form with almost radial symmetry.
25. *Micraster praecursor*. A Cretaceous echinoid from the Upper Chalk. *Micraster* is an irregular heart-shaped form.
26. *Eugnathus orthostomus*. A Jurassic bony fish with numerous teeth and covered with thick rhomboid scales; from the Lower Lias, Lyme Regis, Dorset.

27. Footprints of the primitive dinosaur *Cheirotherium lomasi*, from the Triassic sandstones at Storeton, Cheshire.

28. A skeleton of *Ichthyosaurus communis* from the Lower Lias (Jurassic) of Somerset.

29. A nest of dinosaur eggs (*Protoceratops andrewsi*) found at the base of the Upper Cretaceous in the Gobi Desert, Mongolia.

30. *Iguanodon atherfieldensis*. The skeleton of a beaked dinosaur from the Wealden (Lower Cretaceous), Atherfield, Isle of Wight.

31. The Giant Irish Red Deer which inhabited western Europe during the Pleistocene.

32. *Sphenopteris affinis*. A pteridosperm or seed-fern from the Lower Carboniferous of Scotland.

33. A diorama of the sea floor in Middle Silurian times, showing trilobites, nautiloids, crinoids, corals, bryozoa and brachiopods.

34. A diorama of a late Silurian sea floor, with algae, and a six-foot specimen of *Eurypterus remipes*.

35. A diorama of a Middle Devonian sea floor, with trilobites, straight-shelled and curved nautiloids, single and compound corals, crinoids, gastropods and brachiopods.

36. A diorama of an Upper Devonian sea floor, with a nautiloid, starfish, various types of glass sponges and a primitive fish.

Acknowledgement is made to the following for kindly giving permission to reproduce the photographs: Geology Department, University of Liverpool, for plates 12, 23, 27, the British Museum (Natural History) for plates 14, 15, 28, 29, 30, 31, and The Rochester (New York) Museum of Science and Art for plates 33, 34, 35 and 36. The remainder of the photographs were taken by Miss Elaine Bryant, of specimens at Imperial College.

Illustrations

FIGURES

Illustrations

† *Full page diagrams illustrating modern members of the major phyla of the Animal Kingdom.*

I

A Brief History of Fossil Collectors

Nearly three thousand years ago the hobby of fossil collecting had its beginning in Greece. As far back as 500 B.C. Xanthus of Sardis drew attention to the occurrence of fossils, and on the Island of Cos in the Aegean Sea, it is believed that Hippocrates, the 'Father of Medicine', studied one of the first fossils to be recorded in history. Xenophon (430–357 B.C.), Aristotle (384–322 B.C.) and Strabo (63 B.C.–A.D. 24) were among other Greeks, Romans and Arabs, who, in the next centuries, were to pick up and ponder over fossils. Sometimes they clearly saw in their remains evidence of periodic submergence of land areas, while at other times they believed these fossils to be only the remains of some ancient workers' lunch. Throughout the Middle Ages most Europeans who collected fossils saw in them evidence of men and animals who perished in the Flood of Noah.

The late fifteenth century was to see the birth of fossil collecting as a science. In 1452 there was born in Italy the great artist, scientist and inventor Leonardo da Vinci, who in his later life wrote some notes concerning the origin and meaning of fossils.

As a young man, Leonardo helped to plan a navigable canal in northern Italy, and while supervising the work, came across large numbers of shell, coral and plant remains. Examining these ancient fossils, he said to himself, 'Here are petrified creatures not unlike the existing animals of the sea, and the plants of the

Leonardo da Vinci

field and the wood. These, being dug from gravel beds, must be of great age. Therefore these rocks and shells and plants must have inhabited those waters and valleys.'

One of the great scholars of the next century was Conrad Gesner (1516–65), who, in 1565, completed a bulky work that was the first book to actually illustrate fossils. Gesner had no true conception of the origin of the fossils he sketched, but regarded them as being either the remains of animals or productions of some inorganic process. At this time fossils were usually considered as creatures or objects formed by some plastic force deep within the earth. They were called '*lusus Naturae*', or 'freaks', or 'sports' of nature.

From the sixteenth century onwards, fossil collecting became increasingly popular. The first 'cabinet' or collection of fossils was put together by Georgius Agricola (1494–1555). Agricola's collection was noteworthy, for he carefully gathered all the information he could find, both from a study of earlier authors and from examination of his own specimens. He was also the first man to coin the term 'fossil', although he used this term for everything he dug out of the earth. It took three hundred years for the word fossil to become restricted to mean the remains of prehistoric animals and plants found in rocks and more recent deposits.

Pioneers of this field in the sixteenth and seventeenth centuries often had to recant their published beliefs, as these contradicted religious and traditional ideas. During the next two hundred years many more workers entered the field of palaeontology, as fossil collecting and the study of fossils came to be called. Men like Robert Hooke (1635–1703), Martin Lister (1638–1711), John Woodward (1665–1722) and Johann Gottlob Lehmann (d. 1767) put forward important theories, and advanced the idea that a chronology could be derived from fossil successions. The real surge of progress in palaeontological knowledge began in the late eighteenth century however, and the man who finally changed the 'seminal vapours' of 1698 into the science of palaeontology and stratigraphy was an Englishman named William Smith, the 'Father of English Geology'.

As a young surveyor and engineer, Smith mapped and plotted the course for a canal in Somerset, during which time he noted that the rock layers or strata lay on top of each other like 'so many superimposed slices of bread and butter'. For several years

William Smith

B

17

William Smith walked uncounted miles over the hills and valleys of Gloucestershire, Somerset, Devon and many other parts of the country, collecting fossils and observing geological outcrops. Picking up fossils was not enough however, for he began to trace known fossils (many of which he himself identified and described) within certain rock beds he had plotted on his maps, then to trace the beds themselves from one locality to another, seeing both similarities and variations of the beds.

This work of Smith began the real study of stratigraphy, or the correlation of one geological formation with another through the use of fossils. By this method, long ages of the past could now be shown to leave the stories of their history in successive layers

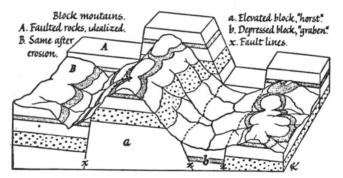

Fig. 1. Showing how rock beds or strata become separated, dissected, and exposed by earth movements and erosion

of rock. Although these successions of strata were not always found to be complete or even similar in every locality, the fossil assemblages they contained always seemed to follow a fixed order or stratigraphical relationship. Thus Smith showed that the fossils themselves allowed a comparison of beds within a given time sequence, and often proved similarity of age between widely separated localities.

A Brief History of Fossil Collectors

In 1816 William Smith published his famous *Strata Identified by Organized Fossils*, and, one year later in 1817, the field of fossil collecting was even more firmly established by the publication of his *Stratigraphical System of Organized Fossils*. On the continent also, many other palaeontologists, including Lamarck, Werner, Schlotheim, Cuvier, Brongniart, Barrande and d'Orbigny, wrote of their own researches and closely approached Smith's correlation principles in their deductions.

The study of fossils in America began towards the latter part of the eighteenth century, when it was still a vast and unmapped wilderness, waiting for the early pioneer geologists to explore its deserts, mountains, and waste lands. Perhaps the most famous in the field of fossil collecting in these earlier days were Thomas Jefferson, Richard Harlan, Jefferies Wyman and Joseph Leidy.

Thomas Jefferson

Jefferson (1743–1826) was a pioneer vertebrate palaeontologist, and kept his collection in the nation's White House, for in 1801 Jefferson was elected President of the United States.

In the eighteenth and nineteenth centuries much valuable collecting and research was carried out by amateurs; local clergy, lawyers and gentry often accumulated large personal collections. By 1830, publications outlining the discovery of new fossil beds, theories concerning the geological development of the earth and stratigraphical correlations began to pour from the presses. The great geological thinker, Sir Charles Lyell, published his *Prin-*

Charles Darwin in middle life — from a little-known portrait in Locy. As a young explorer-naturalist on the 5-year voyage (1831–36) of H.M.S. Beagle, Darwin began the observation and thinking that led to his great theories of evolution.

Charles Darwin

ciples of Geology in 1830, which was followed in 1834 by De La Beche's *Researches into Theoretical Geology*. Next came Sir Roderick Murchison's gigantic volumes on *The Silurian System* in 1839. These, among many other works, formed a stepping-stone to Charles Darwin's (1809–82) great theories on evolution.

One of the most stupendous fossil hunters was an American, James Hall (1811–98) of Albany. In 1836, Hall was appointed as an assistant in the recently established State Survey of New York. Within a decade the fossil collections of the New York State Geological Survey were among the largest in the country. Such industrious collecting was to crystallize into the fifteen monumental quarto volumes in which Hall described and illustrated the fossils of New York. The twentieth century was to see an equally great collector in the person of Charles D. Walcott of the United States National Museum. He discovered the classic Middle Cambrian Burgess Shale of British Columbia, from which he obtained a superb collection of invertebrate fossils.

Today, fossil collectors both famous and unknown, abound in every part of the world. Either as professional or amateur, they continue the quest for the mysterious creatures of the past, always finding strange new treasures in the endless adventure of exploring the rock layers of the earth.

II

Fossils . . . What are They?

A fossil is the remains, or trace of remains, of an animal or plant that has been preserved in the rocks representing the deposits of past geological times. It is preserved over a long period of time by one or other of the various processes described below. The word 'fossil' comes from the Latin verb *fodere*, meaning 'to dig'. From around 1550 to 1800 it was customary to name everything being dug up from the earth a 'fossil', whether it were of mineral or of animal origin.

Types of Fossil Preservation

(1) First we have actual preservation, which, though of rare occurrence, is possible when bacterial action and decay have been prevented. The baby mastodon uncovered in the ice of Alaska only a few years ago is one example of such actual preservation. This almost perfectly preserved mastodon is now displayed in a refrigerated case at the American Museum of Natural History in New York. Other animals have been preserved without any chemical alteration in bogs and oil pits or seepages. This is particularly characteristic of the Pleistocene deposits which were deposited within the last million years. Insects found in fossil resin often appear to be unaltered, but in fact only their hard exoskeleton is preserved.

22

(2) In fossilization by mineralization, the porous shell or piece of bone has all its air spaces and cavities filled in with mineral matter. This has been brought in solution by the water which percolates through the earth, and when precipitated out of solution it fills up such fossils without changing their original shape or substance. This action tends to make it more heavy, at the same time giving it protection.

(3) Replacement is a third method and one of the most common. In this process the original animal substance, that is the shell or skeleton, is gradually dissolved and replaced by a different mineral. Silica often replaces wood in this manner. In corals and shells also, the actual specimens, other than their soft parts, can be entirely replaced by quartz, calcium carbonate, iron pyrites or other minerals.

(4) Carbonization is the process whereby all the elements or organic materials undergo decomposition, leaving only a residue of carbon to record the actual organism. Fossil plants are often preserved in this way.

(5) Moulding, casting and imprinting are closely connected. For example, shells embedded in rock or sedimentary deposits can be dissolved away, leaving a cavity which preserves the actual size and form of the object. In this natural mould percolating sub-surface waters may deposit minerals such as quartz, and so produce a natural cast. Thus sea urchins filled with flint are found in the Chalk.

(6) The tracks of animals are considered to be fossils when they are preserved in soft muds later hardened into rock. Sometimes even impressions of jelly-fish are found in rocks. Fossil burrows, and borings in rocks and in fossil shells, could also be included here.

(7) A coprolite is fossilized excrement or dung, in which can

usually be found scales of fish, or parts of other animals, that were devoured by the animal which dropped it. They can teach much about the eating habits of early forms of life.

(8) Encrustation of leaves, sticks or bones in the mineralized waters of caves or springs may form fossils or tufa. This can commonly be seen in limestone districts.

Conditions which Favour the Preservation of Fossils

(1) Rapid burial in sediments. Dead animals are usually devoured rapidly by scavengers, or are decayed by bacterial action. However, early burial in moist sediments prevents this.

(2) Rapid burial in volcanic ashes. In western America great numbers of dinosaur bones have been preserved by burial in volcanic ash.

(3) Possession of hard body parts, such as bones, shells or outer skeletons (as in crabs).

(4) Uniform temperature conditions, with no rapid freezing, etc.

(5) Presence of highly mineralized ground waters.

(6) Fine sediments make better burial material than coarse.

(7) Quiet conditions of deposition, so that the fossils are not broken up by wave and current action.

III

The Classification of Fossils

The animal and plant kingdoms are divided into many phyla or major divisions, and the fossil record presents the majority of these phyla as recognizable fossils. Some of course are scarce in their geological distribution, their record being so meagre that specimens are known mainly to specialists.

To properly classify the many thousands of different kinds of fossils would take a book vastly larger than this one. Here the main need is to teach the user to classify fossils down at least as far as order or class, and how to identify a few of the very common or unusual fossils down to genus or possibly species. This is sufficient to start a collection of labelled specimens, and you can do the more complete classification later when you have learned how to use the more technical descriptive literature or can take your fossils to an expert or museum and have them more precisely classified. Below is a chart showing the main divisions of animal and plant classification, taking two very common species as examples.

Species	*lupus*	*campestris*
	(wolf)	(yellow mustard flower)
Genus	*Canis*	*Brassica*
	(dog genus)	(common mustard genus)
Family	*Canidae*	*Brassicaceae*
	(dog family)	(mustard family)
Sub-order	*Fissipedia*	
	(land carnivores)	

The Classification of Fossils

Order	*Carnivora*	*Papaverales*
	(flesh eaters)	(poppy order)
Sub-class	*Eutheria*	*Dicotyledoneae*
	(placental)	(2 leaves in embryo)
Class	*Mammalia*	*Angiospermae*
	(milk givers)	(true flowering plants)
Sub-phylum	*Vertebrata*	*Pteropsida*
	(backboned)	(large complex leaves)
Phylum	*Chordata*	*Spermatophyta*
	(a notochord)	(seed plants)

The dog family (*Canidae*) includes such genera as *Canis* (dogs) and *Vulpes* (foxes). The genus *Canis* includes such species as *latrans* (coyote) and *lycaon* (North American timber wolf). Thus, as you move up the column from phylum to family to species and so on, the relationships of the groups become much closer.

(NOTE: As you read through this chapter, refer to the next chapter in which the different earth ages are shown in a geological time scale (p. 66.) This will help you to understand the relationships of the fossils described here and their times of recorded occurrence in the history of the earth.)

CLASSIFICATION OF THE ANIMAL KINGDOM FROM THE FOSSIL RECORD

In the pages that follow, inserted into the text are several charts illustrating the major phyla and classes of the Animal Kingdom. These charts show pictures of modern animals in their proper relationships. In the text, however, fossil animals are described and illustrated as they are related to these modern animals (except that some modern phyla, such as Rotifera and Nemertinea, are so poorly represented as fossils that they are not mentioned here as part of the fossil record). This will not only help you in classification, but will show you evolutionary relationships between ancient and modern animals. It will also make clear what ancient phyla, orders and classes have completely disappeared from the earth (* marks all extinct forms).

You will note that the more primitive animals are usually found in the earliest rocks. This is one of the strong proofs of some kind of evolutionary development of animal life. The chart on page 28 shows in a very simplified form the development of animals from the simple to the complex (evolution) as visualized by scientists. This Theory of Evolution is based on a very great accumulation of evidence that can barely be touched upon in a small book such as this, but the theory is itself in process of evolution and new discoveries each year bring changes to this idea. The struggle for existence with survival of the fittest is the backbone of the theory of evolution, and provides an intelligent solution to the problems concerning the changes from primitive life to more advanced forms, and the disappearance of animal groups (for example, the dinosaurs) which were once prosperous and numerous. Even today the struggle to live and to reproduce continues fiercely, all living forms having survived because of their greater ability.

Phylum Protozoa

These are the simplest of all animals and consist of single cells or a small number of similar cells. The majority are microscopic forms which leave little or no trace when they die. Under this phylum, however, we do find two orders which have left a wealth of fossil evidence; the orders Foraminifera and Radiolaria of the class Sarcodina.

The Foraminifera have shells which are commonly made of

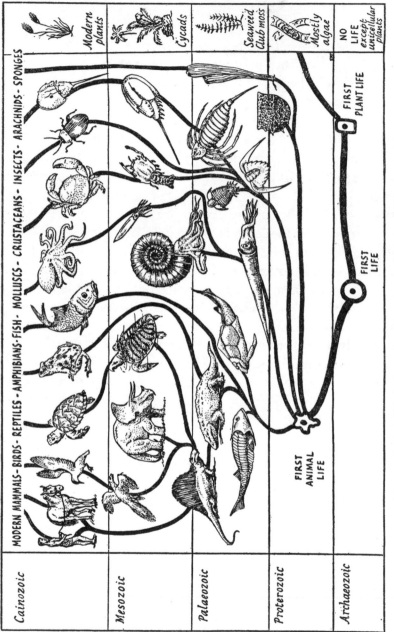

Fig. 2. A simplified chart showing the evolution of life on earth.

calcium carbonate, sometimes silica, and which consist of one, or of a number, of microscopic chambers. These can be arranged in a straight line, in a spiral or in a zigzag pattern. They are the most common form of Protozoa, and many thousands of miles of sea floor are entirely covered with uncountable numbers of their shells. This material is called Globigerina ooze after one of the more common genera.

One of the larger and more easily found of the fossil Foraminifera is *Nummulites* (Plate 1), a discoidal form common in the Barton and Bracklesham Beds of the English Eocene, and which often attains the size of a sixpence. Although rare until Carboniferous times, Foraminifera are found in Upper Carboniferous rocks and persist to the present day.

The Radiolaria build their shells of silica. They are not divided into chambers but occur as globes (Fig. 4) and pyramids of great diversity and complexity, often pierced by holes and ornamented with spines. In England they range from the Ordovician to the present day.

PHYLUM PORIFERA

The sponges belong to this group, and while appearing rather like plants, are actually many-celled animals. They take in food

Fig. 3. Sponge spicules

and water through innumerable pores scattered over their surface, hence the term 'Porifera'. The majority of sponges secrete a skeleton which may be of spicules of calcium carbonate or silica, or of a horny organic substance called spongin. The latter are not preserved as fossils. In some sponges the spicules are held together in a loose meshwork by organic matter; this decays after death, and so only the individual spicules are found (Fig. 3). Other fossil sponges are preserved as entire specimens (Plate 2), for their spicules join to form a continuous network.

Sponges are found in many shapes, from the fairly simple vase shape illustrated, to more complex types with folded walls and tubular projections. Others are mushroom-, fan- or funnel-shaped; spherical, cylindrical or encrusting. Sponges range from the Lower Cambrian to the present, and were very common in Palaeozoic times.

PHYLUM COELENTERATA

The Coelenterata are multicellular animals a little more advanced and complicated than the Porifera. Some are free swimming or single polyps, others form colonies; some secrete skeletons and others do not. Three classes of this phylum are illustrated in one of the charts (Figs. 11–13), and these are the only classes of interest to the fossil collector.

The class Hydrozoa (hydrocorallines) is represented from the Lower Cambrian to the present, and includes such forms as the fresh-water *Hydra*, a simple sac-like polyp. Most are marine, however, and include jelly-fish such as the Portuguese Man of War, encrusting organisms or 'sea mosses' and the *Stromatoporoids which secreted skeletons of calcium carbonate. These are important constituents of Lower Palaeozoic limestones, and are

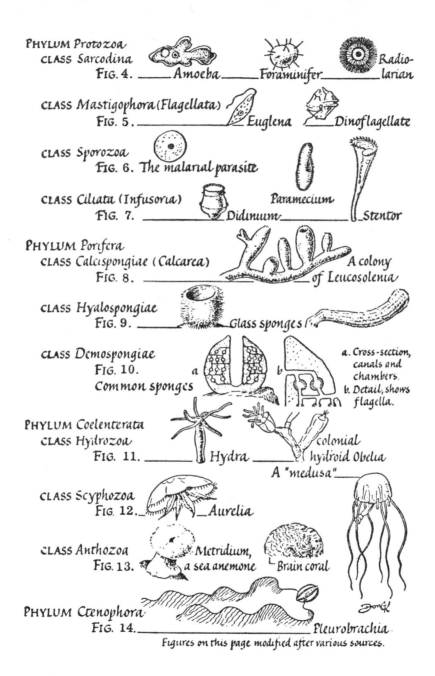

PHYLUM *Protozoa*
CLASS *Sarcodina*
FIG. 4. _____ Amoeba _____ Foraminifer _____ Radio-larian

CLASS *Mastigophora* (*Flagellata*)
FIG. 5. _____ Euglena _____ Dinoflagellate

CLASS *Sporozoa*
FIG. 6. The malarial parasite

CLASS *Ciliata* (*Infusoria*)
FIG. 7. _____ Didinium _____ Paramecium _____ Stentor

PHYLUM *Porifera*
CLASS *Calcispongiae* (*Calcarea*)
FIG. 8. _____ A colony of Leucosolenia

CLASS *Hyalospongiae*
FIG. 9. _____ Glass sponges

CLASS *Demospongiae*
FIG. 10.
Common sponges
a _____ b _____
a. Cross-section, canals and chambers.
b. Detail, shows flagella.

PHYLUM *Coelenterata*
CLASS *Hydrozoa*
FIG. 11. _____ Hydra _____ colonial hydroid Obelia

A "medusa"_____

CLASS *Scyphozoa*
FIG. 12. _____ Aurelia

CLASS *Anthozoa*
FIG. 13. _____ Metridium, a sea anemone _____ Brain coral

PHYLUM *Ctenophora*
FIG. 14. _____ Pleurobrachia

Figures on this page modified after various sources.

found either as encrustations or as hemispherical masses of concentric wavy laminae, crossed at intervals by pillars or rods.

The class Scyphozoa also ranges from Lower Cambrian times, or possibly even earlier. It includes the larger and more conspicuous jelly-fish. Umbrella-like, with a fringe of tentacles, these have no hard parts, but sometimes leave a faint impression in fine-grained sediments under very quiet depositional conditions. Today they are found in fresh as well as salt water.

The class Anthozoa, which includes the corals and sea anemones, is very important to the collector. Corals first appeared in Ordovician times as solitary individuals which secreted a cone-shaped or cylindrical shell, divided internally by radiating partitions called septa. Very similar in fact to the coral in Plate 3, which shows the septa in the calyx or depression at the top of the shell. These Palaeozoic corals were the *Tetracoralla or Rugose corals, which also included massive, compound and branching forms, some of which were important reef builders. Plate 4 shows a compound rugose coral, *Lonsdalia floriformis*, made up of individual corallites. Here the septa are separated from the outer walls of the corallites by a zone of dissepiments, which are small curved plates that usually connect the septa. In the centre of each corallite a columella can be seen.

Figure 15 shows a tabulate coral, in which the tabulae (horizontal plates) are well developed. *Halysites* is a chain coral, and

Fig. 15. *Halysites*, a Silurian chain-coral

Plate 1. *Nummulites laevigatus*. A foraminifer from the Lower Bracklesham Beds, Eocene, Whitecliff Bay, Isle of Wight. The smaller specimen shows the external ornament and the larger specimen has been split open to show the interior arrangement of the chambers in spirally coiled whorls.

Plate 2. *Raphidonema faringdonense*. A vase-shaped calcareous sponge from the Cretaceous Faringdon Sponge Bed at Faringdon, Berkshire.

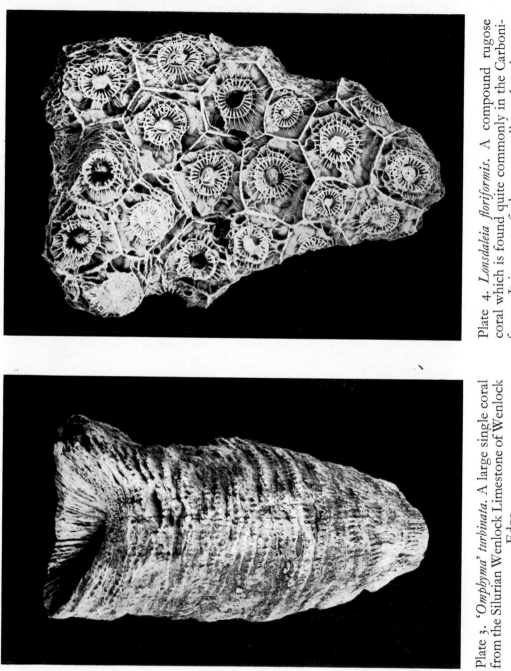

Plate 4. *Lonsdaleia floriformis*. A compound rugose coral which is found quite commonly in the Carboniferous. It is rare to find one as well weathered-out as the specimen illustrated.

Plate 3. '*Omphyma*' *turbinata*. A large single coral from the Silurian Wenlock Limestone of Wenlock Edge.

Plate 5. *Didymograptus murchisonae*. A tuning-fork graptolite from the Ordovician of Abereiddy Bay.

Plate 6. *Eschara pertusa*. An encrusting bryozoan from the Pliocene Coralline Crag at Sudbourne.

Plate 7. Silurian Wenlock Limestone with bryozoan colonies, crinoid ossicles, etc.

Plate 8. A typical decalcified shelly siltstone or sandstone of the Lower Palaeozoic, with brachiopods (*Orthis*, *Chonetes*), crinoid ossicles, etc.

Plate 9. *Epithyris bathonica*. A terebratulid from the Upper Jurassic rocks of Gloucestershire.

Plate 10. *Rhynchonella quadriplicata* from the Jurassic rocks of the Cotswolds.

Plate 11. *Asaphus cf. tyrannus*. A trilobite from the Ordovician rocks near Builth Wells.

Plate 13. *Calymene blumenbachi*. A common trilobite of the Silurian Wenlock Limestone This specimen was collected near Dudley.

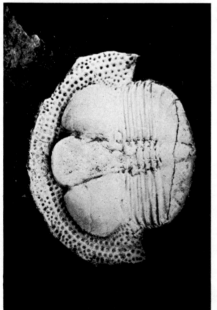

Plate 12. *Trinucleus concentricus*. A specimen found in Ordovician rocks in Trilobite Dingle near Welshpool.

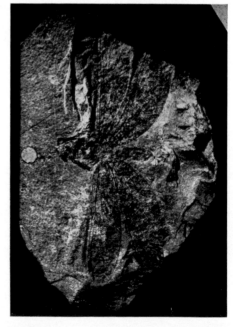

Plate 14. *Heterophlebia buckmani*. A Liassic dragon-fly from the Jurassic rocks of Gloucestershire.

Plate 16. *Venericardia planicosta*. An Eocene lamellibranch from the Bracklesham Beds at Southampton; exterior and interior views. The interior view shows the teeth and sockets and also the two muscle scars.

Plate 17. *Aequipecten opercularis*. A Pliocene scallop from the Coralline Crag at Sudbourne Hall, Suffolk.

Plate 15. A model of *Eurypterus*.

Plate 18. *Voluta spinosa*. A Lower Oligocene gastropod from the Isle of Wight.

Plate 19. *Asteroceras obtusum*. A Lower Lias ammonite from Lyme Regis, Dorset.

with other members of its group such as *Favosites*, *Heliolites* and *Syringopora*, was also an important reef builder in the Lower Palaeozoic.

*Graptolithina

Graptolites were thought for a long time to be a coelenterate group, but one of the more recent theories holds that they are protochordates. Dendroid graptolites (see page 70) such as *Dictyonema* are thought by some to belong to the Hydrozoa, and they have a fan- or funnel-shaped skeleton consisting of numerous radiating branches connected by transverse bars.

Graptolites, now extinct, were floating, marine colonial organisms which secreted a supporting and protective exoskeleton of chitinous material. Each individual polyp making up the stalk or stipe of the colony lived in a small cup or theca. These can be seen in Plate 5, and they make the stipes look like tiny saw blades. The number and the attitude of the stipes varies considerably, and since this group includes a large number of forms which evolved rapidly, graptolites are very valuable for zoning, dating and correlating rocks. For example, 'tuning-fork' graptolites with two stipes like the illustrated *Didymograptus murchisonae* are characteristic of the Lower Ordovician, and monograptids with only one stipe are distinctive of the Silurian.

The exoskeletons are usually fossilized as thin carbonaceous films, and they are found from the Tremadocian to the Lower Carboniferous.

Phylum Polyzoa (Bryozoa)

Polyzoa are superficially like colonies of coelenterate polyps, but are, in fact, much more highly organized. They are very small, almost tubular animals, largely marine and always colonial in habit. They secrete calcareous skeletons which are fixed to the sea floor, and which are built up by many individuals. These colonies may take various forms; the specimens in Plate 7 are largely stem-like branching types, but they can also be massive or encrusting (Plate 6).

The Polyzoa were most common, both in variety of species as well as abundance, during early Palaeozoic times. They appear less abundantly from the Devonian to the present day, and form an involved phylum needing microscopic study to determine even genera.

PHYLUM BRACHIOPODA

Brachiopods are bilaterally symmetrical (equal-sided), inequivalved (two valves of unequal size) marine bivalve shellfish, with shells of chitino-phosphatic or calcareous material. They are either pediculate (with stems or stalks) or are sessile (attached to rocks without stems). The valve (half shell) through which the pedicle emerges is the ventral (lower) valve, and the opposite valve the dorsal (upper). A few pediculate forms with a fleshy muscular pedicle have the ability to burrow in sand and mud, and to move about slowly. The valves are held together by teeth and sockets in articulate (jointed) brachiopods (Fig. 24), but by muscles only in inarticulate (unjointed) brachiopods.

The brachiopod shell remains closed after death, therefore many internal moulds are found (Plate 8), the actual shell having been dissolved away after it has been filled with sediment. Some brachiopods, such as the majority of terebratulids (Plate 9), lack ornament but possess a smooth punctate (covered with tiny

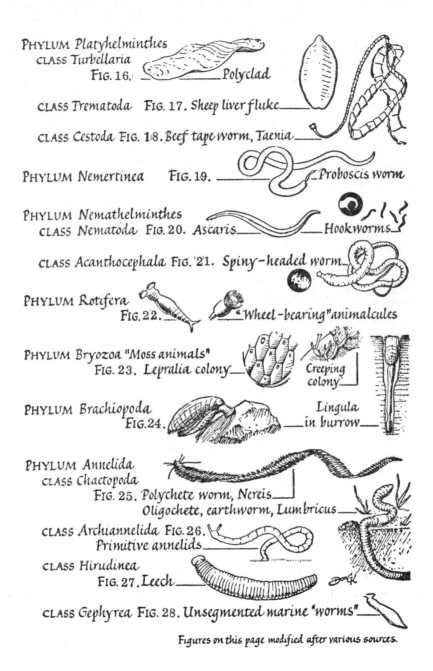

PHYLUM *Platyhelminthes*
  CLASS *Turbellaria*
        FIG. 16. —————— Polyclad

  CLASS *Trematoda* FIG. 17. Sheep liver fluke

  CLASS *Cestoda* FIG. 18. Beef tape worm, Taenia

PHYLUM *Nemertinea*   FIG. 19. —————— Proboscis worm

PHYLUM *Nemathelminthes*
  CLASS *Nematoda* FIG. 20. Ascaris —————— Hookworms

  CLASS *Acanthocephala* FIG. 21. Spiny-headed worm

PHYLUM *Rotifera*
      FIG. 22. —————— "Wheel-bearing" animalcules

PHYLUM *Bryozoa* "Moss animals"
    FIG. 23. Lepralia colony —— Creeping colony

PHYLUM *Brachiopoda*
     FIG. 24. —————— Lingula in burrow

PHYLUM *Annelida*
  CLASS *Chaetopoda*
     FIG. 25. Polychete worm, Nereis
       Oligochete, earthworm, Lumbricus
  CLASS *Archiannelida* FIG. 26.
     Primitive annelids
  CLASS *Hirudinea*
     FIG. 27. Leech
  CLASS *Gephyrea* FIG. 28. Unsegmented marine "worms"

Figures on this page modified after various sources.

holes) shell. Others like the rhynchonellids (Plate 10) are ribbed or even spinose, and have a fibrous impunctate shell.

The Phylum Brachiopoda had its beginning in the Cambrian with a majority of inarticulate forms, although several genera of Articulata are known. The main outburst of genera and species occurred from Ordovician to Devonian times, and then they gradually declined. Brachiopods can be found in most fossiliferous horizons from late Cambrian to late Jurassic, and a few forms continue to live in the warm seas of today.

Phylum Annelida

This phylum includes the common segmented worms such as the modern earthworm. They appear as elongated bilaterally symmetrical animals, with a mouth at one end and the anus at the other. They possess silico-chitinous jaws which are often preserved as fossils, but as they are largely soft-bodied they leave few remains. Some, however, such as *Serpula*, secrete calcareous

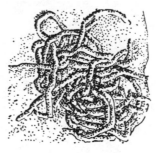

Fig. 29. Worm burrows in a Palaeozoic rock

tubes or cement sand grains together, and they also leave casts, trails and burrows which may be preserved. They are known from the Cambrian to the present day.

The Classification of Fossils

PHYLUM ARTHROPODA

The Arthropoda (jointed limbs) form one of the most interesting groups of fossils, and include the famous class *Trilobita, which is one of the earliest and most specialized of all invertebrate groups. The arthropods are all characterized by having an exoskeleton of hard body armour which protects their delicate inner organs. This armour or skeleton is jointed or segmented in the various body appendages or limbs, which were often specialized organs for locomotion or breathing.

The class Trilobita is the most important group of fossil arthropods. The name arises from the transverse tripartite division into middle and lateral lobes (best seen in Plate 13), well shown by the tri-lobed profile ⌒⌒⌒. They are also divided longitudinally into head, thorax (body) and tail (Plate 11). The head consists of a central glabella, at the sides of which are the simple or compound eyes (Plates 11 and 13), and then the free or fixed cheeks. The whole body is flattened and the head and tail covered by rigid shields. The thoracic segments were articulated however, allowing the animal to curl up for protection. Normally only the dorsal shields are preserved as these were shed periodically. Often, too, these disintegrate as in Plate 11, and only isolated heads, tails or thoracic segments are found.

Trilobites were exclusively marine and lived largely near the sea floor in shallow water. Modifications of some forms however suggest other modes of life. For instance, the development of many spines suggests a free floating existence, and the absence of eyes and the broad head of *Trinucleus* (Plate 12) suggests the habit of burrowing and grovelling in mud. Their forms were diverse and many, and beginning in the Lower Cambrian, their development became less specialized in post-Ordovician times until they

37

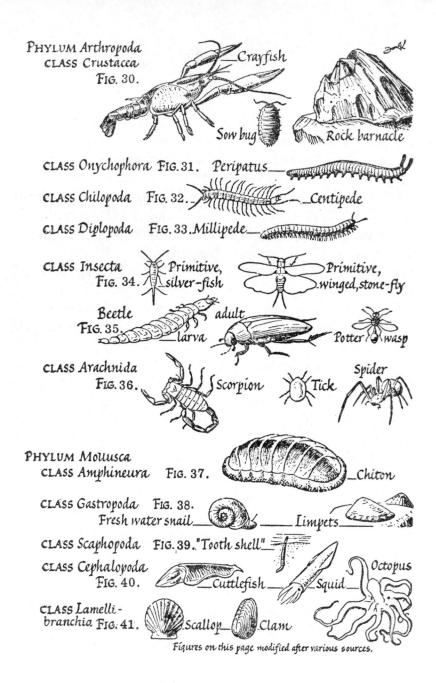

PHYLUM *Arthropoda*
CLASS *Crustacea*
FIG. 30.

Crayfish

Sow bug

Rock barnacle

CLASS *Onychophora* FIG. 31. Peripatus

CLASS *Chilopoda* FIG. 32. Centipede

CLASS *Diplopoda* FIG. 33. Millipede

CLASS *Insecta* Primitive,
FIG. 34. silver-fish

Primitive,
winged, stone-fly

Beetle adult
FIG. 35. larva

Potter wasp

CLASS *Arachnida*
FIG. 36.

Scorpion Tick

Spider

PHYLUM *Mollusca*
CLASS *Amphineura* FIG. 37.

Chiton

CLASS *Gastropoda* FIG. 38.
Fresh water snail Limpets

CLASS *Scaphopoda* FIG. 39. "Tooth shell"

CLASS *Cephalopoda* Octopus
FIG. 40. Cuttlefish Squid

CLASS *Lamelli-*
branchia FIG. 41. Scallop Clam

Figures on this page modified after various sources.

became extinct at the end of the Permian. With the brachiopods, they are the most important fossils of the Lower Palaeozoic, and certainly among the most fascinating.

The class Crustacea is represented by several fossil forms. The sub-order Decapoda includes the crabs, lobsters and crayfish which are so familiar today. The first undoubted occurrence of this group is in the Trias, but they are far more numerous in more recent rocks, and the carapaces and claws of the crab *Xanthopsis*, for instance, are fairly common in the Eocene.

The sub-class Ostracoda are less familiar crustaceans. They appear to be tiny lamellibranchs, but are actually arthropods, for although they possess bivalved shells they also have jointed legs. Most ostracods are too small to be of great interest to the average collector, but they can be valuable to specialists as index fossils. They range from the Upper Cambrian to the present day.

The sub-class Cirripedia includes the barnacles (Fig. 30). While being crustaceans, they differ greatly from the ordinary forms, for these degenerate arthropods cement themselves to shells, rocks or other marine life by means of a calcareous base. Here they wait for the sea to bring them food with the coming of each tide. The first undoubted Cirripedes are found in the Upper Jurassic, although possible forms are known from as far back as the Cambrian. They appear most commonly in shore deposits from the Miocene to the present.

The class Insecta can be divided into two sub-classes: (1) The Apterygota, which consists of four orders of primitive wingless insects (such as the silver fish in Fig. 34); and (2) the Pterygota, which is made up of some forty-one orders of winged insects (such as beetles and flies, see Figs. 34, 35 and Plate 14) and secondarily wingless insects (such as fleas and lice).

The remains of a primitive wingless insect have been found in the Middle Devonian chert of Rhynie in Aberdeenshire. Otherwise the first fossil remains are found in the Coal Measures, where a variety of forms occur. Many are also found in Permian, Jurassic, Cretaceous and later rock formations. Rapid burial by sediments is essential for the preservation of these delicate organisms, and superbly preserved insects have been found in fossil resin (amber), mainly from the Oligocene.

The class Arachnida contains the scorpions and spiders. These are advanced arthropods with a body divisible into a cephalothorax, covered by a carapace, and abdomen (Fig. 36). Scorpions have few fossil representatives, although primitive forms have been found in the Silurian of Lanarkshire, and also in the Carboniferous, Trias and Oligocene. Spiders also are rare as fossils, although here again good specimens in amber are found in the Oligocene.

Fig. 42. An early sea scorpion

The most enormous arachnids, however, belonged to the subclass Merostomata, and were the *Eurypterids (Fig. 42 and Plate 15). They were the terrors of the estuaries and shallow seas of the Silurian, and often exceeded six feet in length. It is probable that they were the cause of the decline in trilobite population during the Silurian and early Devonian, and were great rivals of the first fish. They are only found in Palaeozoic rocks, and the best specimens in this country have been obtained from the Silurian of Lanarkshire.

Another arachnid order, Xiphosura, is found in fossil form, and ranges from the Cambrian to the present. The living representative is *Limulus* or the King Crab, and one of the more common English fossil forms is *Belinurus* of the Upper Old Red Sandstone and the Coal Measures.

PHYLUM MOLLUSCA

This phylum is made up of four major classes, numerous sub-classes, and includes a vast number of invertebrate animals which are similar in organic structure, but differ radically in the form of their shells. There are well over sixty thousand recorded living species and an uncounted number of fossil forms. Their great abundance is due in part to their ability to exist in various types of environment, climate and depths of water. This phylum includes the clams and scallops (Fig. 41); the snails and limpets (Fig. 38); the devil-fish, squids and octopuses (Fig. 40); the tusk or tooth shells (Fig. 39) and the coat of arms or chiton shells (Fig. 37).

The class Lamellibranchia contains the mussels, oysters, scallops and their relatives. As in the brachiopods, the soft body is enclosed in a shell of two valves, but instead of being dorsal and ventral, these valves are placed one on the right and one on the left side of the body. Also, the two valves are almost identical externally, and certainly very rarely show the bilateral symmetry of the brachiopod valves. The shape, size and ornament of the shell can vary enormously.

The valves are locked together by projections of the hinge called the teeth, and these fit into corresponding sockets in the opposite valve. The small teeth under the beak are termed cardinals, and the long teeth parallel to the hinge are called laterals. The number and arrangement of the teeth can also vary, and even forms a basis for classification. *Venericardia*, in Plate 16, has two very large cardinal teeth and one small lateral tooth. The valves are shut by means of a pair of muscles which are attached to precise areas of the shell known as muscle scars. The front one is the anterior muscle scar, and the rear one is the posterior muscle scar.

Most lamellibranchs crawl along the floors of seas, rivers and lakes, and these move with a fleshy foot which is adapted for burrowing or clinging to rock surfaces. Others, such as oysters, cement themselves to rocks, and scallops (*Pecten*, Plate 17) swim by clapping their valves open and shut. In England, lamellibranchs range from the Tremadocian to the present, and are evident in most fossiliferous horizons, especially marine. They are scarce in some periods such as the Ordovician, but abounded in others such as the Cretaceous, when they assumed gigantic and bizarre shapes.

The Gastropoda include the snails, whelks and slugs. Snails usually possess spirally coiled shells with a horny or limy door called the operculum. The spire can be coiled in one plane or it may coil downwards after the first whorl and form a high, pointed spired shell (Plate 18). These variations of coiling and of external ornament are of great value in the classification of fossil forms. Unlike the lamellibranchs, which are largely marine, gastropods live in oceans, fresh water and on land, and like some lamellibranchs, they crawl on a fleshy foot. Gastropods range from the Cambrian to the present, and though in the past they were generally less abundant than lamellibranchs, they now exceed them in number.

The Classification of Fossils

The Scaphopoda, or tooth shells, form a class of the phylum Mollusca (Fig. 39). They have a bilaterally symmetrical body protected by a calcareous tubular shell, open at both ends. They go back to Ordovician times, but did not become common until the Cretaceous. Today they live in fairly deep water, burrowing into mud or sand, where they wait for the ocean tides to bring them food. The ancient Indians used to use shells of the genus *Dentalium* as money, so they are common in Indian burial mounds.

The class Cephalopoda is considered one of the most important by petroleum geologists and palaeontologists, for cephalopods, and particularly ammonites, had a rapid and varied evolution, and so make good zone fossils, important for correlation. Modern representatives include the squid and the octopus (Fig. 40), but more common in ancient seas were the previously mentioned ammonites (Plates 19 and 20), the nautiloids (Plate 21 and Fig. 43) and the belemnites (Fig. 44). Many of these were very highly developed and specialized forms.

The order *Ammonoidea includes the most common cephalopod fossils, and ranged from Devonian to Cretaceous times, with the greatest evolution occurring from Triassic to Cretaceous times. The ammonites have either a coiled (Plates 19 and 20) or straight shell, divided internally into compartments by simple or frilled sutures of varying form, useful for identification and classification. These sutures often attained very great complexity, and they can be seen on the surface of the ammonite in Plate 19. *Asteroceras* is a ribbed form, and *Euhoplites* is decorated with tubercles. In the Cretaceous the ammonites, then a dying race, indulged in a final fling, producing fantastic and irregular forms, including many uncoiled or partly coiled types.

The order Nautiloidea ranged from the Cambrian to the present, and was a more conservative order, with simple septa, and after the Palaeozoic, uniformly coiled shells. Though never very common, the nautiloids (Plate 21, Fig. 43 and page 75) sometimes reached a spectacular size, and were carnivores with long tentacles.

The order Dibranchiata includes the modern squid and octopus, and the extinct belemnites, which had straight, cigar-shaped shells inside the body. It is this inner shell or guard which is preserved as a fossil (Fig. 44). Belemnites range from the Trias to the Cretaceous, but were most prominent during Jurassic times. In this period they sometimes grew to be five or six feet long, but

Fig. 43. An ancient nautiloid

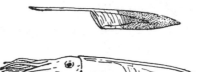

Fig. 44. A fossil belemnite

no specimens of this size are found in Great Britain. They had six, instead of the squid's ten, arms or tentacles, and these arms were covered with hooks instead of suckers. Sometimes these are preserved as a carbonized film.

PHYLUM ECHINODERMATA

This phylum contains seven classes, of which five are shown in the chart, Figures 46–50. The important fossil groups are the *Cystidea, Crinoidea, *Blastoidea, Asteroidea and Echinoidea. While the Echinodermata appear more primitive than either the Arthropoda or the Mollusca, some scientists believe that they show a closer relationship to the next phylum, the Chordata, than do the other two.

Fig. 45. A Silurian fossil cystid, showing the irregularly shaped plates

The class *Cystidea consisted of the most primitive echinoderms, and lived only during Palaeozoic times. They were usually stemmed organisms (Fig. 45) with a calyx (flower-like head) rather similar to that of a crinoid (Plate 22 and Fig. 46), but with imperfect arms and irregularly shaped and arranged plates, which varied in number according to the species. In Figure 45 brachioles (arms) can be seen radiating from the food grooves along which they sent food to the mouth. They were diverse both in structure and in external form, and are usually poorly preserved and rare as fossils.

The class Crinoidea is an important fossil group of the Echino-

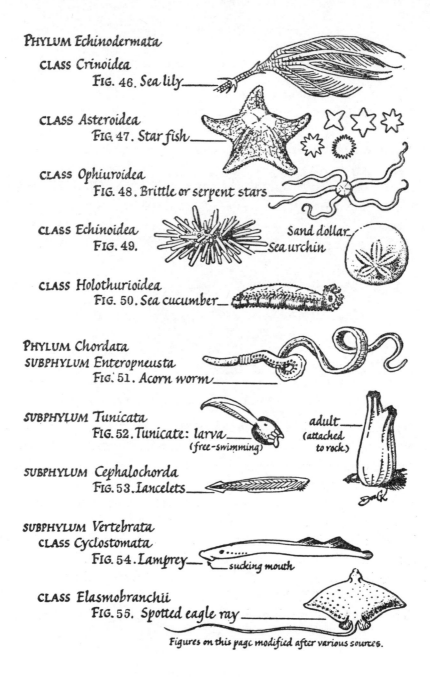

PHYLUM Echinodermata
    CLASS Crinoidea
        FIG. 46. Sea lily_____

    CLASS Asteroidea
        FIG. 47. Star fish_____

    CLASS Ophiuroidea
        FIG. 48. Brittle or serpent stars_____

    CLASS Echinoidea   Sand dollar
        FIG. 49.   Sea urchin

    CLASS Holothurioidea
        FIG. 50. Sea cucumber_____

PHYLUM Chordata
SUBPHYLUM Enteropneusta
        FIG. 51. Acorn worm_____

SUBPHYLUM Tunicata   adult_____
        FIG. 52. Tunicate: larva_____   (attached
            (free-swimming)   to rock.)

SUBPHYLUM Cephalochorda
        FIG. 53. Lancelets_____

SUBPHYLUM Vertebrata
    CLASS Cyclostomata
        FIG. 54. Lamprey___
               sucking mouth

    CLASS Elasmobranchii
        FIG. 55. Spotted eagle ray_____

Figures on this page modified after various sources.

dermata (Plate 22 and Fig. 46). Crinoids each have a calyx from which radiate many feathered arms, strengthened with brachial plates. The calyx, composed of rings of many regularly shaped plates, is borne on a long flexible stalk made up of small circular or pentagonal plates or ossicles. On the death of the animal these usually break up, and loose crinoid ossicles are very common in some limestones, and some can be seen in Plate 7. This long stem served to anchor the crinoid to the sea floor, but some forms are free swimming, such as *_Marsupites_ of the Upper Cretaceous. Crinoids range from the Ordovician to the present, but were of greatest abundance and variety during Palaeozoic times.

The class *Blastoidea closely resembles the crinoids in having a bud-shaped calyx on a short jointed column, but differs from the crinoids and cystids in not possessing arms. The head is made

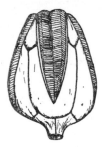

Fig. 56. *Pentremites*, a fossil blastoid which is rare in Europe but found commonly in the Carboniferous of North America

of thirteen main plates, with two outer rings of five plates each. Five food grooves lead to a mouth at the top. In England, the Blastoidea ranged from the Devonian to the Carboniferous, being much more abundant in the latter period.

The order Asteroidea includes the starfish and their relatives. These possess a star-shaped body (Plate 23) with a central plate or disc, and usually five arms covered with plates; very like existing forms in fact (Fig. 47). Some of the plates have movable spines with which they move about and catch their food. The mouth is on the under-surface. Complete fossil specimens are relatively rare, and when they do occur, it is often in 'starfish-beds', where numerous specimens of one or two species or genera are found. They range from the Cambrian to the present.

The class Echinoidea is by far the most common in both number of genera and species and quantity of specimens to be found. Sea urchins are not generally accepted as important index fossils, but some are used as zone fossils in the Chalk, and *Micraster* (Plate 25), especially provides an interesting and chronologically significant record of evolution.

The echinoids bear a test (or outer skeleton) composed of thin, closely joined calcareous plates. As can be seen in Plates 24 and 25, these plates can be divided into narrower columns of ambulacral plates and the wider columns of interambulacral plates. The former have pairs of pores through which small tube feet are protruded and used for locomotion. The large tubercles seen in the figure of *Hemicidaris* form the bases to large and small spines, which usually become detached after death and are often found separately. Echinoids sometimes 'dig' holes in rocks, in which to anchor themselves. The first echninoids appeared in the Ordovician, but their distribution in the Palaeozoic was sporadic. They attained their maximum development during the Cretaceous period.

PHYLUM CHORDATA
EMPHASIZING THE SUB-PHYLUM VERTEBRATA

The most advanced animals of the Animal Kingdom are those with a backbone and spinal cord. These have been placed in the phylum Chordata. This phylum includes primitive animals without a backbone, but having a nerve cord (notochord) running down the length of their bodies from head to tail (Figs. 51–3). The chordates with a backbone are called vertebrates, and are often divided into two super-classes, Pisces (fish) and Tetrapoda (four-footed animals, including however the snakes). The phylum as a whole ranged from the Cambrian to the present.

Vertebrates are often so large that their fossil remains in the rock need to be taken out by experts. The new and inexperienced fossil collector is liable to ruin such specimens, particularly the more delicate bone structures. For this reason it is suggested that if you find such fossils, take out only a small section to show the nature of what you have found, and report your discovery to the nearest university or museum. It is possible that they may allow you to help with the work of digging out these large fossils, if you show yourself willing to co-operate and work with care.

The Super-class Pisces (fish)

The class Agnatha are the jawless fishes, and the best known modern representative of this group is the lamprey eel (Fig. 54). The early Palaeozoic members of this class, the Ostracoderms, had a rigid bony armour covering the front portion of their bodies, and scale-like plates covering the remainder. A complete specimen of *Thelodus* (Fig. 57) has been found in the Silurian of Lanarkshire; this primitive ostracoderm had widely separated

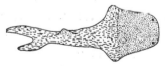

Fig. 57. *Thelodus*. A jawless fish, covered with small scales which lived in late Silurian times

eyes along the front of its head, and the whole body was armed with numerous small stud-shaped scales. These 'skin-teeth' are often found loose in other deposits; in the Ludlow Bone Bed, for example.

The class *Placodermi is an extinct group of primitive jawed fish which appeared in the Silurian and died out before the end of the Permian. These also had extensive bony armour, and included the acanthodian sharks and the arthrodires. The sharks had well-developed spiny fins and were covered with closely packed rhomboidal plates. The head armour of the arthrodires was not continuous with that of the body, but jointed to it by a peg and socket articulation. *Dinichthys* (Fig. 58 sometimes grew

Fig. 58. *Dinichthys*. An arthrodire of the Devonian

to enormous proportions and its armour had apparently sunk beneath its skin and become internal.

The class Chondrichthyes contains the boneless fish, which have skeletons of cartilage, and often an external covering of placoid scales. Ranging from the Devonian to the present, this class includes the true sharks, skates and rays (Fig. 55). They were good swimmers, with long tails and both pectoral and pelvic fins (Fig. 59). Their teeth, both blunt grinding plates and sharp cusps

Fig. 59. *Cladoselache*. A Devonian shark

(Fig. 60) and spines, are fairly common as fossils, especially in the Mesozoic and Cenozoic. By the late Eocene, enormous sharks like *Carcharodon* roamed the seas, sometimes attaining lengths of more than forty feet.

Palaeontologists believe that the amphibians had their beginning in the Osteichthyes (bony fishes). Appearing in the Devonian, these bony-skeletoned fishes were very successful and are thriving today in both fresh and sea water. The early forms had comparatively thick enamelled plates (Plate 26), but these, with the fins and general structure, underwent progressive modification. An interesting group of this class is the sub-class Dipnoi or lung-fish, which were very common during the later Palaeozoic. These fish have a lung bladder through which they can breathe air, and so can live through arid seasons when fish with gills would die. A member of this group survives today in the rivers of Australia.

Fig. 60. A tooth of *Carcharodon*, a giant Tertiary shark

SUBPHYLUM *Vertebrata* (cont'd.)

CLASS *Pisces*
FIG. 61.

CLASS *Amphibia*
FIG. 62. *American toad*___

CLASS *Reptilia*
FIG. 63.

CLASS *Aves*
FIG. 64.

CLASS *Mammalia*
FIG. 65.
Pronghorn
*antelope*___

Sailfish

Desert tortoise

Emperor penguin

Man o' war bird

Gibbon

Pacific
walrus

Figures on this page modified after various sources

The Classification of Fossils

Super-class Tetrapoda

These are the paired-limbed creatures, including the amphibians, reptiles, birds and mammals, and as with the fish, individual bones, teeth, scales, spines and also footprints are more common than entire fossil specimens (Plate 27). The amphibians go back to Upper Palaeozoic time. The reptiles first appeared at the end of the Palaeozoic, dominated the Mesozoic, and, except for the relatively few forms existing today, died out at the end of the Cretaceous. The fossil record shows evolution progressively increasing in complexity.

In the class Amphibia are included the frogs, toads, newts and salamanders; all animals whose blood stays near the temperature of their surroundings. Being half of the water and half of land, they usually spend their infancy as fish-like larvae with gills, but gradually change to adults with lungs, which enable them to live equally well on land or in the water.

The first known amphibians lived in Upper Devonian and Carboniferous times, and were small newt-like animals with quite a complex skull structure belonging to the Stegocephalia group. In the Upper Palaeozoic and Lower Mesozoic larger amphibians, the labyrinthodonts, attained lengths of eight or nine feet, and were clumsy heavily built creatures. Frog-like amphibians are rare as fossils, and none are known to occur before the Upper Jurassic. As well as skeletal remains, amphibians leave trails and footprints in the fossil record.

The class Reptilia, or reptiles, also are animals whose blood keeps a temperature close to that of their environment, but they differ from amphibians by starting life as air-breathing land animals, and in having a covering of scales. All reptiles probably at one time had four legs, but the snakes have lost theirs through a process of evolution (as is shown by vestigial legs in boa-constrictors). Some reptiles, such as the turtles and the extinct ichthyosaurs and plesiosaurs, returned to the water to live, though they never redeveloped the ancestral gills. The ichthyosaur (Plate 28) had a streamlined fish-like shape, and was perfectly adapted for life in the sea. The plesiosaur, however, was a little more clumsily built and not so well adapted, and it is possible that it had limited power of movement on land, where it perhaps laid its eggs. Fossil reptile eggs, probably of dinosaurs, are known from as far back as the Upper Jurassic, and in Plate 29 are dinosaur eggs from the Upper Cretaceous of Mongolia.

The most spectacular reptiles, of course, were the dinosaurs (Figs. 66–8 and Plate 30), which dominated the world during

Fig. 66. *Protoceratops*. A horned dinosaur from the Cretaceous of Asia

Mesozoic times. They originated in the Triassic but were almost extinct by the end of the Cretaceous, possibly because of their very small brains and lack of adaptability to changing conditions.

Dinosaurs assumed many bizarre forms and shapes. There were the sluggish amphibious forms like *Diplodocus* (Fig. 67) which lived in coastal swamps, only occasionally leaving the water which helped to support their enormous bulk. There were peaceful plant-eaters with fantastic armour like *Stegosaurus* (Fig. 68), ferocious carnivores such as *Tyrannosaurus* and weird-looking

Fig. 67. *Diplodocus*. An amphibious dinosaur found in the Upper Jurassic deposits of America

flying forms, the pterodactyls. The mososaurs, closely related lizard-like forms, followed the example of the ichthyosaurs and took to marine life. The theromorphs were mammal-like reptiles which may have been the connecting link between the two groups.

The class Aves, or birds, are rare as fossils. The earliest known are from the Jurassic, and, while having feathers very like the modern bird, these earlier creatures also possessed teeth, scales on the lower part of their legs and a peculiar arrangement of the

Fig. 68. *Stegosaurus*. A herbivorous dinosaur

55

tail feathers (Fig. 69). Their feathers appear in two rows, one on each side of the long tail, unlike the fan-like arrangement of modern birds. The best examples of these reptilian-like birds are to be found in Solenhofen, Germany, and the Niobrara limestone

Fig. 69. *Archaeopteryx.* The oldest known bird, found in the Jurassic

formations of Kansas in America. In the Pleistocene birds become relatively abundant as fossils.

The class Mammalia contains the warm-blooded animals that bear their young alive, have a body-covering of hair, and breathe by means of lungs. They had their beginnings in the Mesozoic when they were a small and insignificant group. They came into their own at the beginning of the Cenozoic, however, after the extinction of the dinosaurs, but the early forms were very primitive, unspecialized and with a small brain (Fig. 70).

The bones of mammals show many interesting changes as

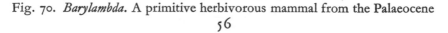

Fig. 70. *Barylambda.* A primitive herbivorous mammal from the Palaeocene

these animals adapted themselves to changing climatic conditions and greater competition from their enemies. For example, the primitive horse (Fig. 71) gradually lost the use of two of its three toes, and developed one toe into the present hoof for faster run-

Fig. 71. *Hyracotherium* (*Eohippus*). A primitive three-toed horse of the Eocene

ning. It also grew steadily larger. At the same time the elephant was developing a trunk and tusks, and the brains of most mammals were increasing in size. Down through the ages also the different grazing animals, such as the buffalo, developed better teeth for grinding up grass and leaves.

With the beginning of the Pleistocene, the mammals evolved into a great variety of forms, the most adaptable of which survived the ice ages and persisted into modern times. The three animals shown below in Fig. 72 were not so adaptable however.

CLASSIFICATION OF PLANTS IN THE FOSSIL RECORD

The Plant Kingdom is abundantly represented by a wealth of excellently preserved plant fossils in coal, shales and sandstones.

Fig. 72. Giant sloth, sabre-toothed tiger and a South American glyptodont

Beginning in Pre-Cambrian times as primitive calcareous algae, they had developed into land plants by the Devonian, and attained great diversity of form and widespread adaptability during the Carboniferous period, when the great coal beds were formed on the sites of ancient swamps.

Many volumes have been written about fossil plants alone. In a small guide-book of this kind, only enough detail can be given to acquaint the reader with the major plant divisions (equivalent to the animal phyla), and some of the more interesting and important fossil plants of the different geological periods. It is interesting to note that the evolution of plants moved along at about the same rate as that of the animals from the simple to the complex. A modern sunflower is probably as complex in its way as a modern ape.

DIVISION I, THALLOPHYTA

This division includes the one-celled plants, the bacteria and algae as well as plants such as fungi and lichens which have no roots, stems, leaves or flowers. Because most of these plants have few or no hard parts, their fossil record is usually scanty.

The sub-division Algae, however, are recorded from pre-Cambrian time to the present, and occur abundantly in some Palaeozoic horizons (rock layers) as shapeless masses or reefs, made up of forms similar to that shown in Figure 73. Also very important are the family Diatomaceae, or diatoms (Fig. 74).

Fig. 73. A fossil alga, consisting of concentric calcareous layers

Fig. 74. Diatoms

Essentially, these are tiny plants enclosed in glass 'boxes', manufactured by the plant from the silica in the water. These protective coverings may take many interesting geometrical forms, which are often preserved in rocks as fossils and sometimes form quite thick beds.

The order Charales (or Charophytes) are a form of algae that become very complex, so much so as to sometimes be called a different division. They have apparent leaves and stems, and a small, calcareous fruiting body (like the fruit in higher plants) that helps the plant to reproduce sexually. These hard fruits are solid enough to be fossilized, and are found from pre-Devonian times to the Pleistocene.

Fig. 75. Fossil spores

The sub-division Fungi, including the mushrooms and bracket fungi, are found as fossils in the Devonian and in even older rocks. In some Carboniferous shales they have been found preserved as spores (Fig. 75).

Division II, Bryophyta

This division includes the mosses and liverworts, which have leaves, or leaf-like forms, but no true roots or flowers. They are found on damp earth, tree bark, or floating on water. The oldest fossil liver-worts are found in the Upper Carboniferous Coal Measures, but the lack of hard parts of members of this group makes them quite rare as fossils.

DIVISION III, PTERIDOPHYTA

This includes those plants that have vascular tissue (specialized plant tissue for carrying liquid in tubes), leaves, stems and roots, but do not possess flowers, cones or seeds.

The class Lycopodiales includes the extinct Palaeozoic 'scale trees' and the modern club mosses. The latter occur today on our hills as inconspicuous trailing plants with the sporangia on the leaves usually formed into small cones. The narrow leaves appear spirally. The ancient 'scale trees' (*Lepidodendron*), however, were often over one hundred feet high. Their fossils can always be recognized by the way in which the prominent leaf scars are regularly spaced over the bark (Fig. 76).

The class Articulatales includes the modern order Equisetales, or horsetails, which grow two to three feet high and have peculiar jointed stems with tiny scale-like leaves at the joints. Some of the

Fig. 76. The bark of a fossil scale tree

ancient relatives or ancestors of these plants, however, like the Carboniferous genus *Calamites* (order Calamitales), grew a foot in diameter and go up to thirty-five or more feet in height. Their ribbed and jointed trunks are distinctive when found as fossils. At one time they covered vast swampy areas, but by the end of the Permian period they had died out.

61

The order Filicales includes the true ferns. These all possess well-developed vascular tissue and distinct roots, stems and leaves. However, they reproduce by means of spores, and have no true flowers or fruits. Large collections of fossil ferns may be made from most Carboniferous Coal Measure shales. Collecting is especially excellent along mine dumps or the spoil-banks of open-cast coal mines. The genera most commonly found are *Pecopteris*, *Neuropteris* and *Alethopteris*, though some genera found may be seed ferns (see below).

DIVISION IV, SPERMATOPHYTA

This division includes all the plants with true cones, flowers and seeds, and widespread fossil plants belong to the order Pteridospermae or seed ferns (Plate 32). These plants had large leaves or fronds bearing seeds, and often became very large; perhaps up to one hundred feet tall. They then looked more like palms than ferns. They were most extensive in the late Palaeozoic and were the oldest plants with true seeds. The Bennettitales were Mesozoic plants very like the living cycads, but their reproductive organs resembled those of the flowering plants.

The sub-division Gymnospermae includes the modern conifers, ginkgos and cycads as well as some very ancient trees called Cordaites (Fig. 79) which lived from Devonian to Permian times. These were tall trees with large strap-like leaves, and with the seeds borne naked in open cones or catkins.

The Ginkgos (order Ginkgoales) are tall trees with broad fern-like leaves (Fig. 77), and primitive seeds borne in pairs. They appeared late in the Palaeozoic and continued to the present.

The order Cycadales (Fig. 78) includes trees of ancient and

modern types with short trunks, a palm-like crown and large seed-bearing cones.

The genus *Sequoia* of the order Coniferales was very widespread in the Miocene, and the order includes the familiar firs, pines, yew

Fig. 77. A fossil ginkgo leaf

Fig. 78. The trunk of a fossil cycad

Fig. 79. A cordaite tree

and monkey-puzzle tree. The latter had almost world-wide distribution in the Jurassic and Lower Cretaceous.

The sub-class Angiospermae includes the true flowering plants. A primitive form is known from the Middle Jurassic, but only in the Upper Cretaceous did they become widespread. From then onwards the angiosperms were a dominant element of the flora everywhere, and still are today.

IV

A Geological Time Scale

Geological time has been calculated by a number of methods, of which the uranium-lead method is one of the best, especially for estimating the age of very old rocks. Such ages can be determined by analysis of certain minerals in some igneous and metamorphic rocks. These minerals contain a radioactive element of uranium, which disintegrates at a constant rate, giving off helium and leaving lead as the end product. Since the rate of uranium disintegration is known, it is possible to determine how long the parent rock has been in existence by estimating the relative proportions of uranium and lead in a given rock.

The age and duration of geological periods and formations can then be calculated by correlating sedimentary rocks with near-by dated igneous rocks. Lately several new methods of deducing rock age have been developed, including Carbon 14 techniques. These are used only for rocks a few tens of thousands of years old. Carbon 14 is a special molecule of carbon that acts in the same way as uranium by losing half its mass at the end of a definite period of years. As the rate of change is known the rock age can therefore be determined. The methane gas proportionate method can be used to tell the age of coals, etc., in which methane gas has been stored in pockets in the rock.

Geological time has been broken down by the geologist-palaeontologist team into five major divisions, each of which can

Plate 21. *Nautilus.* A specimen of Lower Cretaceous age.

Plate 20. *Euhoplites proboscideus.* A Gault (Cretaceous) ammonite from the Isle of Wight.

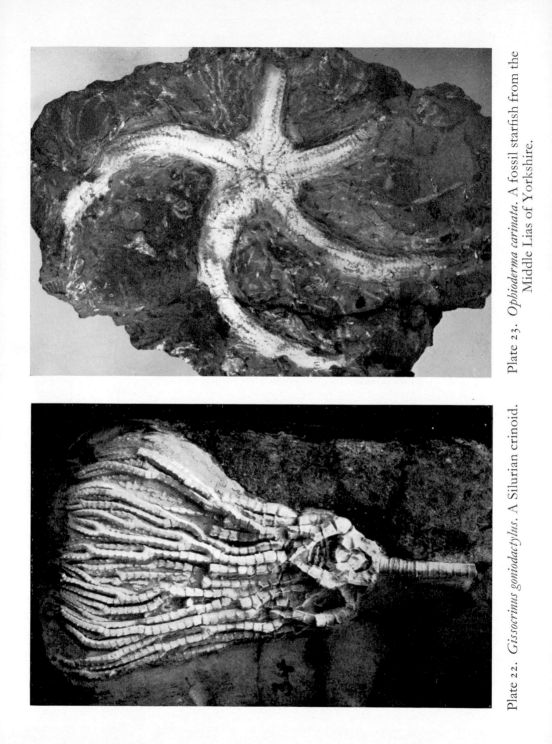

Plate 23. *Ophioderma carinata*. A fossil starfish from the Middle Lias of Yorkshire.

Plate 22. *Gissocrinus goniodactylus*. A Silurian crinoid.

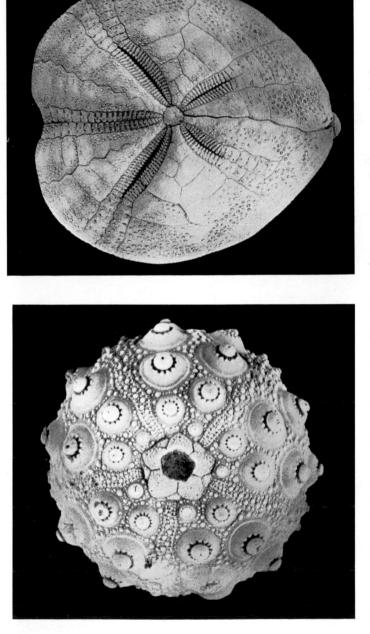

Plate 24. *Hemicidaria intermedia*. A Jurassic echinoid from the Coral Rag at Colne, Wiltshire. *Hemicidaris* is a regular form with almost radial symmetry.

Plate 25. *Micraster praecursor*. A Cretaceous echinoid from the Upper Chalk. *Micraster* is an irregular heart-shaped form.

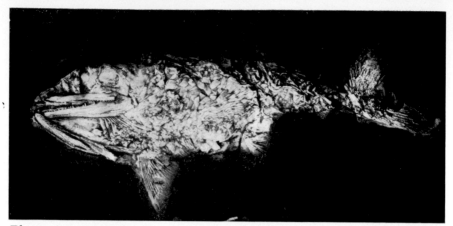

Plate 26. *Eugnathus orthostomus*. A Jurassic bony fish with numerous teeth and covered with thick rhomboid scales; from the Lower Lias, Lyme Regis, Dorset.

Plate 27. Footprints of the primitive dinosaur *Cheirotherium lomasi*, from the Triassic sandstones at Storeton, Cheshire.

Plate 28. A skeleton of *Ichthyosaurus communis* from the Lower Lias (Jurassic) of Somerset.

Plate 29. A nest of dinosaur eggs (*Protoceratops andrewsi*) found at the base of the Upper Cretaceous in the Gobi Desert, Mongolia.

Plate 30. *Iguanodon atherfieldensis.* The skeleton of a beaked dinosaur from the Wealden (Lower Cretaceous), Atherfield, Isle of Wight.

Plate 31. The Giant Irish Red Deer which inhabited western Europe during the Pleistocene.

Plate 32. *Sphenopteris affinis*. A pteridosperm or seed-fern from the Lower Carboniferous of Scotland.

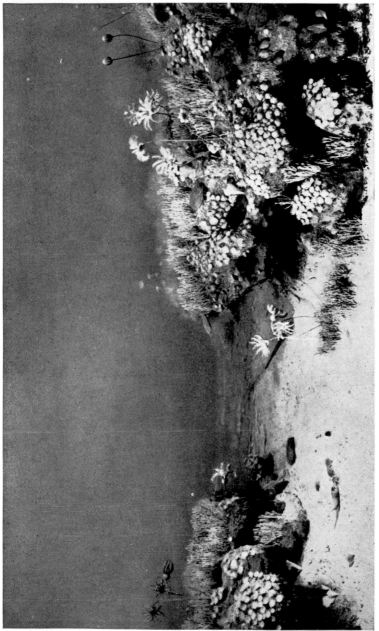

Plate 53. A diorama of the sea floor in Middle Silurian times, showing trilobites, nautiloids, crinoids, corals, bryozoa and brachiopods.

Plate 34. A diorama of a late Silurian sea floor, with algae, and a six-foot specimen of *Eurypterus remipes*.

Plate 35. A diorama of a Middle Devonian sea floor, with trilobites, straight-shelled and curved nautiloids, single and compound corals, crinoids, gastropods and brachiopods.

Plate 36. A diorama of an Upper Devonian sea floor, with a nautiloid, starfish, various types of glass sponge and a primitive fish.

be split into periods. Of the major divisions only three, the Palaeozoic, Mesozoic and Cainozoic eras are of concern to the fossil collector.

Geological time is thought to have begun about two thousand and five hundred million years ago in the Archaeozoic Era, or at the theoretical origin of the earth. Study carefully the geological time chart (Fig. 80) so that you can understand the outline picture of the geological history of the world in general and the British Isles in particular. As each era is described in the pages that follow, you will find at the beginning of the description a diagram showing some of the probable land conditions of the British Isles at that period of geological history. Also shown are drawings in silhouette of some common or characteristic animals and plants of each period. As you read about these plants and animals, refer constantly either to the preceding chapters or to the index for help.

Fig 80: CHART OF GEOLOGICAL TIME

Geological Systems	Duration in Mills. of Years	Basic Facts of Each Period
QUATERNARY ERA	1	AGE OF MAMMALS and rise of birds and flowering plants.
Recent Period	1	Post-glacial epoch; milder climate; growth of human culture; last of mammoths and mastodons die.
Pleistocene	1	Much glaciation; floras and faunas similar to present, but arctic species lived farther south; sabre-toothed tiger, giant sloth, etc., died out; early men.
TERTIARY ERA (Cenozoic)	60	
Pliocene	15	Some mountain building; cooling climate; elephants very numerous; hoofed mammals also numerous, including single-toed horses; apes and man-apes appear.
Miocene	20	Mountain building, e.g. Alps and Himalayas; volcanic activity in N. America; warm climate; modern mammal types flourish; forests reduced as the grasslands spread.
Oligocene	10	Seas shrank; building of the Alps began; climate warm and temperate; beginning of higher mammals and modern insects and flowers.
Eocene and Palaeocene	25	Local outpourings of basaltic lava; very warm climate; archaic mammals existed and the primitive ancestors of modern mammals appeared.
MESOZOIC ERA	125	AGE OF REPTILES
Cretaceous	70	Mild climate cooler and drier; flowering plants and insects more numerous; dinosaurs dominant, but, with the ammonites, died out at the end of the period; mammals increased in number.
Jurassic	30	Very warm climate; conifers, cycads and ginkgos common; first crabs; ammonites abundant; many dinosaurs develop and the first birds and mammals appear.

66

Basic Facts of Each Period

Geological Systems	Duration in Mills. of Years	Basic Facts of Each Period
Triassic	25	Dry desert conditions; scale trees, cordaites, etc., die out, but ferns, cycads, etc., develop; first flying reptiles and sea reptiles.
PALAEOZOIC ERA	325	AGE OF INVERTEBRATES
Permian	25	Warm, rather drier climate; primitive cycads and conifers; reptiles and bony fish appeared; insects became more modern.
Upper Carboniferous	35	Warm damp climate; vast forests of ferns, scale trees, etc.; larger amphibians and many large insects; sharks and cephalopods numerous in the seas; Hercynian Orogeny (Uplift) at the end of the period.
Lower Carboniferous	20	Warm climate; warm widespread shallow seas with coral reefs, bryozoa, etc.; small amphibians on land and beginnings of fern and scale tree forests.
Devonian	45	Earth movements and volcanic activity continued; warm climate; land plants spread; sea scorpions, fish and cephalopods in the seas.
Silurian	30	Warm climate; Caledonian Orogeny (Uplift) began at the end of this period; widespread shallow seas with common corals, molluscs, crinoids, etc.; fish and eurypterids; first land plants.
Ordovician	70	Widespread seas; warm climate; first fish, and rise of corals, bryozoa, etc.; cephalopods developed rapidly.
Cambrian	100	Widespread seas; trilobites and brachiopods dominant.
PRE-CAMBRIAN ERAS	1700+	A succession of widely varied conditions; a little simple life at the end of the pre-Cambrian.

AGE: Era	AGE: Period and Epoch	Group and Formation	Kind of Rock	Prevailing Colour	Thickness in Feet
Mesozoic	Triassic	Shinarump congl.	Conglomerate	Brown	25
Mesozoic	Triassic	Moenkopi	Shale and sandstone	Red	480
		UNCONFORMITY			
Palaeozoic	Carboniferous: Permian	Kaibab limestone	Limestone and sandstone	Gray, buff and red	525
Palaeozoic	Carboniferous: Permian	Coconino sandstone	Sandstone	Light buff	350
Palaeozoic	Carboniferous: Permian	Hermit shale	Sandy shale	Red	225
Palaeozoic	Carboniferous: Permian	Supai formation	Sandstone and shale with some limestone	Red and gray	825
		UNCONFORMITY			
Palaeozoic	Carboniferous: Miss.	Redwall limestone	Limestone	Gray stained red	450 to 500
Palaeozoic	Devonian	Temple Butte ls.	Limestone and sandstone	Pale purplish	0–36
		GREAT UNCONFORMITY			
Palaeozoic	Cambrian (Tonto Group)	Muav limestone	Sandy shale and limestone	Gray	100
Palaeozoic	Cambrian (Tonto Group)	Bright Angel shale	Sandy shale	Greenish gray	450 to 650
Palaeozoic	Cambrian (Tonto Group)	Tapeats sandstone	Sandstone	Brown	225
		GREAT UNCONFORMITY			
Proterozoic	Algonkian	Unkar and Chuar groups of Grand Canyon Series	Sandstone and shale with some limestone; contains sheets and dikes of lava	Mostly red	0 to 12000
		GREAT UNCONFORMITY			
	Archean	Vishnu schist	Schist, granite, and gneiss	Dark gray	Not known

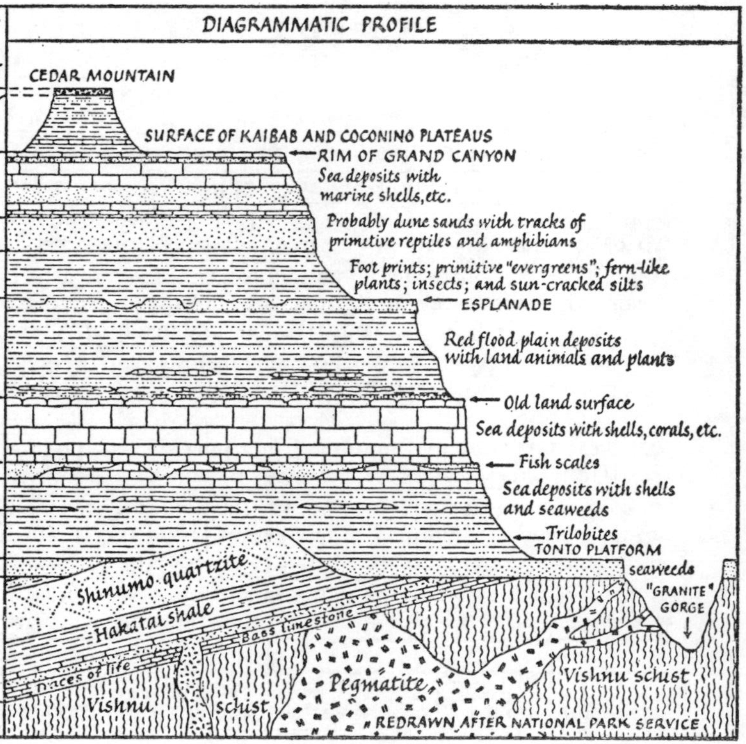
DIAGRAMMATIC PROFILE
CEDAR MOUNTAIN
SURFACE OF KAIBAB AND COCONINO PLATEAUS
RIM OF GRAND CANYON
Sea deposits with marine shells, etc.
Probably dune sands with tracks of primitive reptiles and amphibians
Foot prints; primitive "evergreens"; fern-like plants; insects; and sun-cracked silts
ESPLANADE
Red flood plain deposits with land animals and plants
Old land surface
Sea deposits with shells, corals, etc.
Fish scales
Sea deposits with shells and seaweeds
Trilobites
TONTO PLATFORM
seaweeds
"GRANITE" GORGE
Shinumo quartzite
Hakatai shale
Bass limestone
traces of life
Vishnu
schist
Pegmatite
Vishnu schist
REDRAWN AFTER NATIONAL PARK SERVICE

Fig. 81. A cross-section of the Grand Canyon in the United States showing the thick succession of rock exposed and the stratigraphical divisions. There is no comparable section in Great Britain.

PRE-CAMBRIAN ERAS

Geology and Climate: Pre-Cambrian time is often divided up into the Azoic, Archaeozoic and Proterozoic eras. These cover the time span from the origin of the earth to the beginning of the Cambrian, estimated at more than fifteen hundred million years. During this time the earth gradually cooled and solidified from a hot gaseous state until a land crust formed, and water vapour condensed as rain. Into the resulting rivers and seas weathered debris of the crust was carried and deposited to eventually become stratified rock. These very early rocks later became deformed and altered by heat and pressure associated with subsequent earth movements. At least nine periods of earth movement occurred before Cambrian times, during which mountain ranges were formed and then gradually worn down during the intervening quieter periods. The Pre-Cambrian gneisses, slates, schists and volcanic rocks suggest that Pre-Cambrian landscapes were ever-changing barren scenes of transient mountain ranges, deserts, volcanoes and steaming lava flows.

Life must have originated in the warm seas of late Pre-Cambrian times. No good fossils are found, however, as they were largely soft-bodied forms which left only burrows or imprints. Some Pre-Cambrian limestones contain calcareous layered structures thought to have been due to algae or bacteria. Imprints of jelly-fish, worms and horny brachiopods also occur, and there are problematical forms such as *Charnia masoni*, a frond-like impression found in the Pre-Cambrian rocks of Charnwood Forest.

PALAEOZOIC ERA

CAMBRIAN PERIOD

The Cambrian period is of great significance as the earliest period in which good fossils are found. It is named after Cambria, the Roman name for Wales, where this system was first studied.

Geology and Climate: At the beginning of this period there was a little mountain building in some parts of the world, but on the whole it was a time of quiet erosion with shallow seas gradually encroaching on much of the land. The sea covered most of the British Isles area, and locally, vast quantities of muds and grits accumulated in slowly sinking troughs or geosynclines.

The climate was probably warm, for sponge-like Archaeocyathids, suggestive of warm waters, are found in many widely-separated parts of the world.

Animal Life: A large variety of invertebrate animals were in existence by the beginning of the Cambrian. Brachiopods and trilobites became the dominant forms, but there were also sponges, jelly-fish, radiolaria, primitive echinoderms, molluscs and worms.

Plant Life: The only plants recorded in Cambrian rocks were the calcareous algae, a type of seaweed.

Ordovician Period

Geology and Climate: Before the end of the Cambrian the seas began to retreat, and several new areas of dry land appeared. At the beginning of the Ordovician they advanced again, but it is believed that land ridges remained between Wales and Ireland, and in the Midlands. Sediment continued to accumulate in the geosynclinal troughs, one of which lay across Wales, and the other across southern Scotland. Volcanoes were active in North Wales, Scotland and the Lake District at various times during this period. In North America, however, deposition had been almost continuous, and the seas continued to advance until they withdrew towards the end of the Ordovician.

Most areas had warm, perhaps tropical climates, and many limestones were formed in the shallow marginal seas. Local ice-caps seem to have existed in Norway and South America however.

Animal Life: Invertebrates became much more varied and numerous, but the brachiopods and trilobites were still the most important forms, together with the branched graptolites, which now inhabited the seas in vast numbers. Other new forms included the corals, sea urchins, starfish proper, primitive blastoids, calcareous bryozoa, ostracods and foraminifera. Sponges thrived in the shallow waters and the molluscs, especially the cephalopods, developed rapidly, with *Endoceras* attaining a length of fifteen feet. The first vertebrate remains, those of bony, armour-plated fish, are found in the Ordovician of America.

Plant Life: This still consisted largely of various seaweeds.

SILURIAN PERIOD

Geology and Climate: Vast thicknesses of sediment continued to fill up the two geosynclines, which were now distinctly separated by a land barrier. Earth movements began, at first on a small scale, and some areas were alternately elevated and then covered by the sea again; a shallow sea covered the Midlands in the late Silurian. Vulcanicity was less common than in Ordovician times, but there was still a little activity in Gloucestershire, the Mendips and Pembrokeshire. In America, too, volcanic activity lessened, and here also there was alternation of low-lying land with shallow seas.

The climate appears to have been warm and mild over the greater part of the world, and there are local indications of desert conditions in some continental areas.

Animal Life: The animal life of the period certainly suggests warm seas, for in the clear shallow marginal waters there occurred prolific growth of algae, corals, crinoids, stromatoporoids and bryozoa; all lime-secreting organisms and often forming vast reefs (the Wenlock Limestone, for example). Also in these shallow waters lived many trilobites, rare sea urchins, cystids and molluscs, and in deeper water accumulated the floating animals such as the graptolites (mostly monograptids) cephalopods and small crustaceans. Eurypterids and primitive bony fish lived in estuaries, lagoons and fresh water.

Plant Life: Seaweeds and other algae were still abundant in the shallow seas, but in the Upper Silurian deposits of Australia have been found the first known land plants, very simple lycopsids (a kind of clubmoss).

DEVONIAN PERIOD

Geology and Climate: At the end of the Silurian and during most of the Devonian, large-scale earth movements, accompanied by much volcanic activity, caused the gradual uplift of vast mountain ranges and large land masses. In Europe these movements are called the Caledonian Orogeny. The relics of the great mountain chain produced by this orogeny can now be seen in the mountains of Scotland, Wales, the Lake District and Ireland. The initial weathering and erosion of these mountains produced vast quantities of coarse and fine sediment which were carried and deposited in inland basins and vast coastal deltas. One of these deltas covered most of the Welsh Borderlands and part of Wales, and was periodically submerged by the sea and at other times was virtually desert. A shallow muddy sea with local limestone reefs covered Devon and Cornwall, and there was also a little volcanic activity in this area.

The climate at this time was semi-arid and very warm, but some areas must have had a very heavy rainfall to cause such vast accumulations of rock detritus.

Animal Life: Reef-building corals and stromatoporoids still flourished in shallow seas, and sponges, crinoids and starfish were locally abundant. Early ammonoids or goniatites also appeared, with coiled shells and crimped septa. Brachiopods were still the most common invertebrate form. The graptolites proper had disappeared, cystids were dying out, blastoids and echinoids were rare and only a relatively few genera of trilobites remained in existence.

Many new types of animal appeared, including air-breathing forms such as the mites and wingless insects. One remarkable feature of the Devonian was the rapid evolution and spread of the vertebrates, and of the fish in particular. The Devonian is often called the Age of Fishes. The heavily armoured Ostracoderms were numerous, but there now appeared large sharks and true fishes, though the bodies of the latter were covered with bony plates. One fish (*Osteolepis*, a crossopterygian) possessed a body covered with scales, while a later fish of this same order (*Eusthenopteron*) could breathe air, had stout fins with which it could move on land, and had conical teeth with much infolding of the enamel. All these characteristics showed an animal that was in transition from a true fish to an amphibian. Such a fish (of which the modern lung-fish are living examples) could crawl from one shallow river to another. Towards the end of the Devonian, clumsy salamander-like amphibians appeared.

Plant Life: For the first time there was evidence that the land now had an extensive cover of vegetation. The plants also underwent great change during the Devonian, and forms included scale trees, various ferns, seed ferns and primitive evergreens in which the leaves were blade-like instead of needle-like.

A Geological Time Scale

Geology and Climate: During Lower Carboniferous times most of Europe lay under a shallow sea, scattered with large and small islands and atoll-like reefs. Much calcium carbonate was precipitated and later hardened into limestones. Northern Scotland was land at this time, and was partly a delta on which sufficient forest growth was maintained to subsequently produce coal seams. The sandy and muddy deposits of south-western England indicate a rapidly subsiding geosyncline, while in northern England, the shelf sea and its accumulating limestones was locally replaced by more rapidly sinking unstable areas in which shales accumulated.

The climate must have been warm over most of the world, for compound corals are of widespread occurrence.

Animal Life: The shallow seas, rich in lime, supported many corals, brachiopods, foraminifera, crinoids, molluscs, sea urchins and bryozoa. Spirifers and productids were the most common brachiopods, blastoids and silicious sponges were common locally, holothuroids (sea cucumbers) made their first appearance, and goniatites and early forms of nautilus were also common. Dendroid graptolites now die out, and trilobites were becoming extinct and were probably the prey of sharks. Zoning of the Lower Carboniferous in England is based on the occurrence of corals and brachiopods.

Plant Life: Scale trees (lycopods), ferns and seed ferns dominated the Lower Carboniferous swamps, while in the sea the calcareous algae built atoll-like reefs which are most important in some horizons.

UPPER CARBONIFEROUS PERIOD

Geology and Climate: There was renewed uplift at the beginning of the Upper Carboniferous, and northern Scotland, southern England and part of the Midlands became dry land. A Scottish-Pennine delta came into existence, and its forested swamps are represented by the coals and peat-earths found today. These swamps would periodically subside, be invaded by the sea and then built up above water-level once more by the deposition of sediment. The cycle would then begin again. The Millstone Grit which underlies the Coal Measures consists largely of a rhythmic series of shales and gritstones laid down in a fluctuating deltaic environment, and at this time a vast Pennine delta spread out into the sea to the west and to the south. There was a little vulcanicity in the Midland Valley of Scotland.

The climate in the northern hemisphere was a moist tropical or equatorial one, but less is known about the southern hemisphere, where it is believed that South America, Africa, India and Australia were joined to make the vast continent of Gondwanaland. Parts of this continent were ice-covered, however, and glaciation was widespread by the beginning of the Permian.

Animal Life: Limestones were again laid down, though only locally, with a shelly fauna very similar to that of the Lower Carboniferous. The foraminifer *Fusulina* was a striking newcomer, and the blastoids now became extinct. The sharks dominated the seas, and bivalve molluscs were now common in the brackish waters of the deltas and coal swamps. Forms such as *Anthraconauta* and *Carbonicola* are often abundant in Coal Measure Shales.

Fishes were abundant, though the armoured ostracoderms had disappeared. Their successors were the heavily scaled and modern looking palaeoniscoids. On the land amphibians were still progressing, as is shown by their fossilized skulls, skeletons and footprints. They grew very much larger, some reaching ten feet in length and weighing five hundred pounds or more; these were the labyrinthodonts, sprawling creatures with splayed legs, webbed feet and sharp widely-spaced teeth. Insects dominated the air, appearing in greater variety and size than ever before or since in history, including gigantic cockroaches and dragonflies. There were also numerous spiders, land scorpions and centipedes.

Plant Life: The land forests grew in greater and greater luxuriance, with giant ferns, seed ferns, giant tree rushes of the genus *Calamites* and slender lepidodendrons, with strap-like leaves and triangular leaf scars, all building dense jungles. Beneath them grew thick undergrowths of smaller fern-like plants, horsetails and creepers. *Sigillaria*, with vertical ribs and vertical rows of leaf scars (called scales), was a scale tree related to the lepidodendrons, but with larger, more blade-like leaves, a thicker trunk and less spreading branches. All these plants contributed to the formation of immense coal beds.

A Geological Time Scale

PERMIAN PERIOD

Geology and Climate: At the end of the Carboniferous and beginning of the Permian there was another great mountain-building episode, the Hercynian Orogeny. Mountains were raised up and there was much volcanic activity, especially in Scotland and Devonshire. The British Isles at this time were part of an arid or semi-arid continent, with outwash screes and sands being deposited on uneven desert surfaces or carried by temporary streams and rivers into larger delta fans. Arms of the sea became cut off by warping of the crust, and as the inflow from their desert surrounds was negligible, they gradually dried up, leaving salt deposits. One such sea, part of the Zechstein Sea that covered northern Europe, spread over the Pennines in Upper Permian times. In America also there were widespread desert conditions, and the Appalachians were raised up with much volcanic activity. Separating Gondwanaland from Eurasia at this time was the geosynclinal sea called the Tethys.

Permian climates seem to have been very diverse. The red beds and salt deposits of the northern hemisphere indicate hot dry conditions, while in Gondwanaland to the south, there were ice caps, which later retreated and warmer conditions allowed the growth of the *Glossopteris* flora and the formation of coal seams. On the whole, however, it is thought that climates generally became cooler at the end of the period.

Animal Life: Marine faunas were most profuse in the shallow seas that remained connected with the oceans, and are best known from the Tethys region. Globular or spindle-shaped foraminifera (fusulinids) were so numerous in these seas that some Permian limestones are entirely composed of their shells. Among the new brachiopods were the highly specialized spiny productids (which are almost a sure sign of Permian rock beds) and the coral-like *Richthofenia*. Both the fusulinids and the productids, as well as the rugose corals, the fenestellids (lacy, fan-shaped bryozoans) and the trilobites which had been so abundant in earlier periods, gradually became extinct with the closing of Permian times. Blastoids became abundant in the East Indies before dying out at the end of the period.

The belemnoids appeared and the ammonites throve in the more open seas and were becoming subject to rapid evolutionary changes. Many marine animals of the shallow seas found themselves trapped and overwhelmed by the advancing deserts, and similar drastic changes during this period caused the extinction of many forms, the progressive dwarfing of others, and forced many to radically change their form and habits in order to survive. Primitive bony fish lived in fresh water and certain sharks roamed the seas. The acanthodians became extinct, however.

On land considerable evolutionary changes were in progress. A great variety of reptiles, better suited to the drier climates than the amphibians, began to appear. The majority lived on land, but some were partly aquatic. Most were clumsy waddling creatures, though a few began to develop agility in running. Most were small but a few grew to be ten or more feet long. Some developed into beaked types generally living on plants, and others evolved spiked teeth for flesh-eating. Of special interest were the finbacked reptiles of Texas (the pelycosaurs), which possessed long rows of spines connected by skin which rose like a sail from their backbones. Most advanced were the mammal-like reptiles (theromorphs), with teeth becoming differentiated into canines, in-cisors and molars. It is possible that the later mammals evolved from these. During the Permian, insects became generally smaller and the modern orders began to appear. Conspicuous among these were the true bugs, the cicadas and the beetles, the latter with four stages in their histories.

Plant Life: The swamp-dwelling trees and plants of the Car-boniferous began to die out in the early Permian, as more arid conditions prevailed. By late Permian the huge scale trees were all but extinct, as were the cordaites and giant ferns. The true coniferous trees began to take their places, as well as primitive cycads. Of the older kinds of trees that lived successfully through most of the period, the lepidodendrons were the most con-spicuous.

MESOZOIC ERA

TRIASSIC PERIOD

Geology and Climate: The continents again consisted largely of deserts with scree-covered mountains, dune-covered plains and temporary lakes and delta fans produced by occasional heavy rains. Southern England possibly had a higher rainfall than the north, for here the pebbles in the rocks are more rounded and there is evidence of rivers flowing from the south into south-western England. There seem to have been small oases and even swamps supporting thick vegetation, but on the whole, the red beds and salt deposits found, indicate hot dry conditions. The Tethys Sea continued to exist, but the greater part of Europe was land at this time. America, too, was arid, and also had considerable volcanic activity in the north-east.

The climate in the Trias must have been generally hot and dry, and faunas certainly suggest that the seas were warm.

Animal Life: The opening of the Mesozoic by the Triassic period saw the appearance of many new groups of life, both on land and in the sea. The corals developed a new type, the hexacorals, which still exist today. The brachiopods continued abundantly at first, and the rhynchonellids and the terebratulids flourished, only to diminish at the end of the era. Bivalve molluscs such as mussels and oysters became numerous and larger than ever before. Among the cephalopods the ammonites continued in abundance, becoming larger and many developing most complex suture lines. However, all ammonites died out near the end of the Mesozoic, possibly due to attacks by the new marine reptiles. The extinct relatives of the cuttlefish, the belemnites, flourished.

Arthropods evolved the first lobster-like crustaceans, and sea urchins and starfish were clearly becoming related to more recent types. The first carnivorous fish-shaped reptile, the ichthyosaur, appeared and became adapted to life in the oceans. Later came the thick-bodied, slender-necked plesiosaur, catching fish by surprise rather than by speed.

Reptile footprints are abundant and well preserved on the surface of some rock beds, and the marks of raindrops covering vast slabs of sandstone tell of heavy showers which were followed by drying and baking of the ground by the hot sun. Land reptiles continued to expand both in size and variety, being less dependent on water than the amphibians and therefore more able to sur-

F

vive under desert conditions. The first of the early dinosaurs evolved, as well as many mammal-like creatures. The Karroo Sandstone formation of South Africa is the richest bone-bearing deposit of this age in the world. It is probable that the earliest true mammals may have evolved from reptiles before the end of the Triassic period. Carnivorous reptiles became swifter on foot and sharper toothed.

Plant Life: Not many fossil plants are preserved from this period. Ferns, conifers and cycads developed in the northern hemisphere, and in the south, Gondwanaland still kept its distinctive flora of seed ferns (Thinnfeldia, etc.).

JURASSIC PERIOD

Geology and Climate: In Rhaetic times in northern Europe the seas transgressed across the Hercynian continent and deposited marine limestone and shale beds, forming a transition between the Trias and the Jurassic. In the Lower Lias the sea deepened and shales were deposited, but shallower conditions followed in the Middle Jurassic, and limestones, sands and reefs became common. The mountains of the Permo-Trias had now been reduced to low hills and flat-lying ground, which was largely submerged by this shallow Jurassic sea, but which locally or temporarily gave way to estuarine or deltaic conditions as, for example, in Yorkshire. Scotland remained an island for much of the period, and at the end of the Jurassic the sea retreated completely from the British Isles. Very characteristic of the Middle

Jurassic are the oolitic limestones composed of countless minute calcareous egg-shaped pellets, produced by precipitation of carbonate of lime around a nucleus, and rounded by constant agitation of the wave movements in shallow water. Many of these oolites have a fairly high iron content and are important as ores. There was continued deposition in the Tethys geosyncline, and in America there was a long period of gradual erosion, and some vulcanicity which preceded the uplift of the Sierra Nevada range.

The climate seems to have been generally warm and mild; deserts were far less common and rainfall had increased in most regions.

Animal Life: The hexacorals that had started in the Triassic were now abundant, some appearing as simple cup corals, while others such as *Isastraea* were compound. These latter grew in such profusion that they formed reefs, usually with a distinctive associated fauna of molluscs. Hydrozoa and calcareous sponges were also important reef builders in some areas. The cephalopods (squids, nautiloids, etc.) were the most distinctive invertebrates of this and subsequent periods. The ammonites had a great resurgence in this period, after a bad decline at the end of the Trias, and developed many intricate fluted shells with a delicate pearly lustre, which were usually coiled, ribbed and divided inside by frilled septa. Their modes of life varied; some crawled on the sea floor while others swam near the surface. It is due to their extreme abundance in this period that the ammonites are used to identify and correlate the different beds of the Jurassic throughout the world. The belemnites also became very numerous in the muddy seas, and their bullet-shaped internal shells are common fossils of the period; some grew to a length of five or six feet.

Crinoids then, as today, liked to live together in large groups. These were rooted to the sea floor, while others were stalkless and free-swimming. Sea urchins were abundant in Europe and Asia, though less common in North America. *Hemicidaris* was common, and *Clypeus* is relatively abundant in the oolites of the Cotswolds. Crabs appeared for the first time, while arachnids (spiders) inhabited the shallow waters of Germany, France and parts of the Middle East.

Primitive bony fishes, some with thick enamelled scales, and sharks and skates were much in evidence and similar to modern kinds. The dominant animals in the seas, however, were the aquatic reptiles, which preyed on the fishes and the cephalopods. The plesiosaurs roamed the seas with the ichthyosaurs and the latter gave birth to free-swimming young and had sharp conical teeth adapted for seizing fish.

On land, insect life included grasshoppers, beetles, dragon-flies and termites, as well as the earliest known moths, flies, saw-flies and ants. Fresh-water snails were sometimes so abundant that they formed thick limestone or 'marble' beds. A good example of this can be seen on the south coast of England, where shells of *Viviparus* make up the Purbeck Marble. The slow and clumsy amphibians of earlier times were probably killed off by the more aggressive reptiles, but smaller, quicker amphibians such as frogs and toads began to appear.

Dinosaurs and the flying pterodactyls became more numerous on the land, while in shallow waters crocodiles and turtles were dominant. Many dinosaurs had become enormous. Some such as *Diplodocus, Brontosaurus, Cetiosaurus* and *Stegosaurus* were veget-able eaters, whereas others such as the terrible *Megalosaurus* and *Allosaurus* had long claws and sharp teeth for flesh-eating. The pterodactyls of this time had developed the power of flight but retained all the characteristics of reptiles. Another reptilian stock evolved a feathered type of bird, with scales gradually modifying into feathers, but retaining the teeth and jointed tail of the reptile.

The first true mammals began to appear in the Jurassic. They were primitive creatures, no bigger than rats, and perhaps living in woodlands. Their teeth were adapted for feeding on insects and fruits, but some may have eaten reptile eggs.

Plant Life: In the warm seas of the Jurassic red calcareous algae were common. The land plants of this period were varied and abundant, with forests consisting of primitive conifers, cycads, tree-ferns and maidenhair trees (our living *Ginkgo* is a representative of this group). The true flowering plants had not yet appeared, but there were, however, a few problematical flowering plants.

CRETACEOUS PERIOD

Geology and Climate: The early Cretaceous or Wealden deposits found in southern England are a series of clays and sands which accumulated as deltaic beds on the margins of swampy coastal plains. Clays such as the Gault Clay must have been deposited when the sea was deeper, while the greensands accumulated in shallower water. Open sea invaded Norfolk, Lincolnshire and Yorkshire from the east, and marine deposits are found in these areas. In Upper Cretaceous times what is known as the Cenomanian Transgression occurred, and most of the British Isles became covered by the mainly shallow Chalk Sea. Most people are familiar with the Chalk deposits, which are generally white and free from detritus, consisting almost wholly of calcium carbonate. It has been estimated that it accumulated very slowly, perhaps at the rate of one foot in thirty thousand years, and in parts of Britain is one thousand feet thick.

In America there were coal-forming swamps, and in Upper Cretaceous times the Rocky Mountains were pushed up and the sea retreated southwards. There is evidence of glaciation on Australian plateaux of this time, but much of the land that surrounded the Chalk Sea appears to have been desert.

In spite of the irregularities mentioned above, the climate again seems to have been mild on the whole, for there is evidence of abundant vegetation in Greenland and North America.

Animal Life: By Cretaceous times invertebrate evolution saw the arrival of nearly all the modern orders. In the seas both calcareous and siliceous sponges were abundant. Reef corals were not so numerous and were more localized than before, but solitary corals were quite common. Bryozoa were very abundant in some areas and certain Chalk horizons are largely composed of them. Brachiopods became less abundant and still consisted largely of rhynchonellids and terebratulids. Lamellibranchs were very common and they assumed strange and more massive forms; *Gryphea* became very large and *Exogyra* with the curved oyster-like shell was abundant. One group, the Rudists, assumed a conical coral-like form, and even formed reefs in the Tethys region. Coiled ammonites were abundant in early Cretaceous times, but towards the end of the period developed uncoiled and irregular shells and gradually died out; belemnites also died out. Both regular and irregular sea urchins are very common especially in the Chalk where they are used as zone fossils.

Crabs, lobsters and floating crinoids were common in the muddy marine beds of America, while in Europe they mainly inhabited the chalky horizons. The present-day rare coelacanth *Latimeria* probably had ancestors in the Cretaceous, together with the coelacanth *Macropoma*. The coelacanths were supposed to be completely extinct until a remarkable member of this family was recently captured off Madagascar. Mosasaurs (scaled marine reptiles that could extend their mouths to swallow large animals as the snakes can) soon took the place of the ichthyosaurs of the Jurassic, but the plesiosaurs were still numerous. Both preyed on the abundant bony fishes in a manner similar to our present-day rays and sharks.

Pterodactyls, with a wing-span of twenty feet or more, inhabited some coastal cliffs, since their hollow, thin-walled bones and general body-shape made it best for them to launch themselves into flight from high places. The early true bird *Hesperornis* was a powerful swimmer and diver of these times that caught its prey, mostly fish, with long-toothed jaws. Impressions of jelly-fish and resting areas of belemnites have also been found in Cretaceous sandstones and limestones.

On land the dinosaurs continued to dominate life, with *Tyrannosaurus* the most terrible of flesh-eaters, with a height of nearly twenty feet and a length of about forty feet, as well as six-inch teeth and powerful claws. *Triceratops* (three-horned) and *Trachodon* were among the enormous plant-eaters. Mammals were inconspicuous and small, but primitive marsupials and insectivores had appeared. At the end of the Upper Cretaceous the dinosaurs (as well as the ammonites and some other important invertebrates) began to disappear in what has been called the 'great dying'. A change of climate may have caused this, and other possible causes are disease or the eating of reptile eggs by mammals, and similar competition from advanced forms of animals.

Plant Life: Cycads, conifers and ferns were still the dominant

87

forms of plant life during the early Cretaceous. In the middle Cretaceous, however, the higher flowering plants or angiosperms began to appear, and by the end of the period the vegetation was essentially modern. The new flowers and fruits brought a vast new food supply to many animals.

TERTIARY ERA

PALAEOCENE AND EOCENE PERIODS

Geology and Climate: At the end of the Cretaceous most of north-west Europe became land, and the Chalk deposits suffered considerable erosion. Subsidence then occurred again, and shallow seas spread over the land from which rivers brought great quantities of sediment and built vast deltas until a new land surface was raised above sea-level. Then the process began all over again, and so alternating fresh-water and marine deposits were laid down on the eroded surface of the Chalk. The largest marine transgression occurred in the Middle Eocene. Some areas sank more quickly than others and formed basins in which thicker deposits accumulated (such as the London and Paris Basins).

In Scotland and Ireland, and also in the Arctic and parts of India, there were great outpourings of basaltic lava which cooled and formed vast plateaux. These basalts can be seen today in the Hebrides and at the Giant's Causeway in Antrim. The Tethys Sea persisted, and in late Eocene times it is thought that a strait connected it with the Arctic Ocean and so separated Europe from Asia. Some earth movements occurred in the Tethyan region, connected with the later Alpine orogeny. In America also there was at first much erosion of the mountains, and then shallow seas became widespread in the centre of the continent and on the Pacific coast.

The Eocene faunas suggest a tropical climate in the British Isles, and a connection with the warm waters of the Atlantic. Tropical and temperate conditions were far more widespread than at present, although glaciers covered some high mountainous areas, as in western North America, where the Rockies continued to grow in height.

Animal Life: Among the numerous invertebrates of this period were the nummulites of the class Foraminifera, having round, flat and comparatively large calcareous shells (Plate 1). The shells of dead nummulites built thick beds of limestone on the sea floor (the Great Pyramid of Gizeh in Egypt was built of nummulitic limestone), and they lived in profusion in the Tethyan ocean. The major part of the Eocene invertebrate fauna was almost modern in character. Bivalve molluscs (such as oysters, mussels and cockles), cowries, worms, snails and bryozoa were abundant both in variety of species and numbers of individuals. There were also simple corals, a few nautiloids and cuttle-fish, sea urchins and starfish. Crabs were the dominant crustaceans in Eocene and later seas. Two unusual groups of mammals also roamed the Eocene seas; the early whales or zeuglodonts, which were carnivorous, and the sea-cows (*Sirenia*) which fed on seaweed. Among the reptiles, the crocodiles and turtles were coming into their own in lakes and rivers. Fish, with very few exceptions, were similar to living forms.

On land the toothed birds had died out, but an equally strange bird, the huge and flightless *Diatryma*, roamed about. Mammals in the Eocene were at first small like the modern hedgehog. Gradually they grew larger, more specialized and became dominant on land, with almost all the modern orders such as carnivores, primates, etc., well represented. However, what are known as 'archaic mammals', including some strange horned types, like the immense *Uintatherium*, were dominant in this period. These and other herbivores are easily identified in the fossil form by their teeth, which grew into cutting folds with distinctive patterns for each kind.

In many places the ancestors of the elephants, camels, rhinoceroses, horses, cows and pigs, began to appear. All were unspecialized and much smaller than they became later. The elephants spread from Africa, while the horses had their beginning in America, migrating to Europe as *Hyracotherium*, or *Eohippus*, the dawn horse. This early horse, no bigger than a fox-terrier, had front feet with four toes, suited to marshy ground, and tiny teeth for browsing. The creodonts, or ancestors of the modern carnivores, lived upon the plant-eaters, although they were even more primitive in character, being small-brained and reptile-like.

Plant Life: Floras had now acquired a very modern aspect, for although ferns and conifers were common, flowering plants and deciduous trees were dominant. Tropical forms occurred in southern England at this time, and temperate forms with conifers, vines and oaks farther north.

OLIGOCENE PERIOD

Geology and Climate: Marine and fresh-water conditions still alternated, but on the whole the seas shrank and many former areas of deposition became lagoons or lakes. The Oligocene in Great Britain is largely represented by the estuarine marl and limestone deposits in the Isle of Wight and the Hampshire Basin. Europe was connected with Asia at one stage in the period, and the latter was joined to America. In the Tethys geosyncline the vast accumulation of sediments began to be compressed into islands and ridges, and so the building of the Alps began.

The climate still remained warm and temperate, although some continental areas were showing signs of cooler conditions for the distribution of animals and plants needing mild winters became more restricted.

Animal Life: The larger foraminifers, including *Nummulites* and *Lepidocyclina*, still flourished in the open seas, while corals and sponges took part in the building of reefs in tropical zones. Echinoids continued to be abundant, and the irregular form *Clypeaster* became more common. Crabs and barnacles (especially *Balanus concavus*) were also much in evidence, and many thousands of bivalve sea shells, principally scallops, have been collected from late Oligocene deposits.

In the Baltic region of Germany, and a few places in America, pine resin hardened to imprison many thousands of Oligocene insects, showing that most of the modern orders were then present. Fossilized remains of termites have been found in fresh-water beds, and land and fresh-water snails spread widely.

The mammals were now becoming very modern in appearance and included the bats. Elephants were small, with short trunks and with tusks short also, but present in both upper and lower jaws. Primitive horses such as *Mesoshippus* were hardly any larger than sheep, but the teeth were becoming modified for grazing. Most hoofed mammals were forest browsers because grasslands had only just begun to appear. *Palaeotherium*, an odd member of the horse family which resembled a tapir, lived in north-west Europe at the beginning of the Oligocene, and in America the queer titanotheres soon reached gigantic size and then became completely extinct. Other animals such as camels, deer and pig-like forms grew in size.

Plant Life: In parts of Europe, swamps supported forests which later formed deposits of brown coal, but on the whole forests were dwindling. There were, however, widespread red-woods in Greenland, Alaska and Asia. Palms and other forms flourished round the Tethys in sub-tropical conditions, and grasslands were increasing to support the numerous herbivores.

MIOCENE PERIOD

Geology and Climate: No Miocene deposits are known in Great Britain, which during this period was a land area undergoing erosion and suffering from some earth movements which were related to the Alpine orogeny. Indeed, the main events of this period were the building of the Alps and the Himalayas by the folding and thrusting of the Tethyan deposits. This was accompanied by much volcanic activity and increased erosion due to increased rainfall. The Tethys Sea shrank in size, and survives as the present Mediterranean, and at times the North Sea was connected to the Atlantic. Asia now finally became joined to Europe, and in north-west America there were great volcanic fissure eruptions and vast lava plateaux were formed.

During the Miocene the climate became more temperate and tropical forms retreated southwards.

Animal Life: In the seas *Nummulites* had died out but other large foraminifera like *Lepidocyclina* still flourished, together with the algae, lamellibranchs, gastropods and bryozoa. Sea urchins included the heart-shaped *Schizaster* and also *Clypeaster*, and they spread through the warm seas and became quite abundant and diversified; *Micraster*, however, appeared for the last time in the Miocene. The nautilus *Aturia* attained universal distribution before it became extinct at the end of the period. Radiolaria and diatoms also formed extensive deposits.

Bony fishes continued in abundance and variety of forms, and sharks also increased in number, with a species of *Carcharodon* approaching a length of sixty feet. The air was filled with most forms of insect life. Flightless birds reached great size and became fierce carnivores in South America and elsewhere, while primitive penguins, including one species as tall as a man, lived in Antarctica.

Miocene horses had smaller toes, and teeth with higher crowns than earlier forms, and so were better adapted to the new grasslands. Also the first antlered deer, the first ape and the first horned rhinoceros are found in the Miocene, and ancestors of the elephants suddenly appeared in Europe, and later spread to North America. The small sabre-toothed tiger, leopard and lion cats, bear and the ancestral dog were among the common carnivores.

Plant Life: Swamp cypress, oak, maple, hickory and redwood were common trees in North America, and the forests were still more reduced in size as the grasslands increased.

A Geological Time Scale

Geology and Climate: At the end of the Miocene earth move-ments and mountain building occurred in the Alps, Juras and Carpathians; associated block-faulting and subsidence also occurred, and some land disappeared below the sea, giving the northern continents the geographical outline which differed little from that seen today. The Black Sea and the Caspian Sea are survivors of a larger Miocene land-locked sea, and subsidence in north-west Europe gave rise to the present North Sea which formerly had covered much of East Anglia and the London Basin. The Rhine delta, of which the Thames seems to have been a tributary, then built out into the south-western part of the North Sea. There was some volcanic activity in central France.

Climatic conditions were not very different from those of to-day, but towards the end of the period the climate became cooler.

Animal Life: The invertebrate life was very similar to that of today, though there were some warm water types, now extinct, and in the shallows of the North Sea bryozoan reefs formed. Fresh-water molluscs were abundant, and in south-western Europe the snails of the genus *Viviparus* evolved highly ornate and varied shells. The giant shark *Carcharodon* still inhabited the seas, as did the toothed whale *Balaenodon*.

Among the mammals the elephants were more numerous and widespread than in any other period, some attaining enormous size. In Europe apes and man-apes had spread widely, some now leaving the forests to hunt animals in the savannahs. The horse

94

Hipparion now had feet in which only the central toe touched the ground, its two side toes having become functionless. Herds of these wild horses abounded in the grasslands. Giant buffaloes, huge ground sloths, wolves and larger sabre-toothed tigers appeared in this period, and bears also reached a large size.

Plant Life: There was a general retreat of much plant life to the south as the period got colder. In America, for example, the sequoia moved down from the mountains and the north to the coast of California. The flora of Europe contained many species now confined to Asia and North America, and the maidenhair tree *Ginkgo* survived in Germany until the end of the period and then disappeared from Europe.

QUATERNARY ERA

Pleistocene Period

Geology and Climate: The Quaternary is divided into the Pleistocene, which includes the Great Ice Age, and the Holocene or Post-glacial period in which we are now living. The Pleistocene is called the Great Ice Age because, with the general cooling of the climate much of northern Europe and North America became covered by great ice sheets. At various times, however, conditions became warmer, and the ice would retreat to mark what is known as an interglacial period. The Pleistocene can be divided into four main glacial periods and three interglacial periods. The most extensive glaciation of the British Isles prob-

95

ably occurred during the second glacial period, and its extent is shown in Figure 82.

The chief centres of ice dispersion in north-western Europe were Scandinavia, the Highlands and Southern Uplands of Scotland, the Lake District, Wales and north-western Ireland. The Scandinavian ice sheet was the largest of these, and it occupied most of the North Sea during the Pleistocene.

During the glacial periods the sea-level was lower and Great Britain was joined to the mainland of Europe; during inter-glacial periods, however, when the ice melted and added to the volume of the sea, its level rose until it was higher than that of the present day. These fluctuations of sea-level are indicated by the drowned valleys, submerged forests and raised beaches that one can now see around parts of the British coast. Also, the great weights of ice on Europe and North America caused the land masses to be pressed down; when the ice melted the land began to rise slowly once more, and in Scandinavia this recovery still continues.

The ice sheets were fringed by a belt of tundra with sparse vegetation, and in summer the streams from the melting ice would deposit vast quantities of clay and sand. Also, when the ice retreated it left its load of boulders, clay and gravel as moraine, boulder clay deposits and drumlins, often forming a very uneven topography.

The Alps were covered by a separate ice cap, but here also four distinct periods of glaciation can be determined. The greatest area of Pleistocene glaciation was that in North America, where there were three main centres of ice dispersal; all Canada, the Northern States and the mountainous regions were ice covered.

Animal Life: Most Pleistocene marine invertebrates were identical with living species, but had a different distribution. In

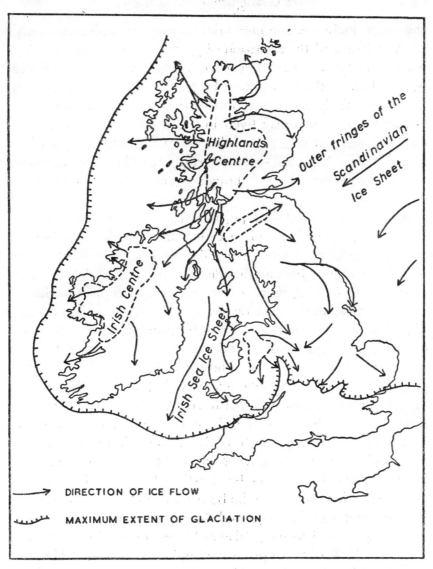

Fig. 82. A map of Great Britain showing the maximum extent of Pleistocene glaciation, the main directions of ice flow and the major ice dispersal centres.

the early Pleistocene, more arctic types of mollusca in this country indicated the approach of glacial conditions, and colder water invertebrates such as certain species of foraminifera were more widespread and occurred farther south. Fresh-water molluscs were fairly abundant, and during interglacials the more southerly forms of today lived in the waters of Britain. However, the onset of adverse conditions caused stunted growth of many species. All in all, land and fresh-water invertebrates were similar to modern forms though were not so abundant or diversified.

Birds were of modern type, but there were peculiar species such as the Great Auk, now extinct, and the flightless Moa of New Zealand. Of the land mammals, most of the present species were in existence during the Pleistocene, but had a different distribution. Indeed, there are very complex records of life in some districts, as the climatic changes led to many migrations. Most land animals were driven south during the glaciations, and during the last glaciation, reindeer, arctic fox and steppe marmots came down as far as southern England. During the interglacials, however, hippopotamuses lived along the Thames, and lions and hyenas roamed farther north. Various types of true elephants and true horses were quite common, and oxen appeared in Asia. Some animals, such as the woolly rhinoceros, woolly mammoth and cave bear became adapted to living on or near the ice; these animals have now been extinct for some thousands of years, and other animals to die before the end of the Pleistocene were the sabre-toothed tiger and the giant sloth.

During the Pleistocene, Palaeolithic man spread quite widely over the Old World, and primitive implements are found in river gravels, and wall paintings and drawings occur in caves in Africa, Asia and Europe. Skeletal remains are rare, however, and the evolutionary record incomplete, but late Pleistocene men were of a modern type.

Plant Life: Plants were essentially the same as at present but the oncoming of glacial periods forced most species far to the south, with an occasional northward migration whenever conditions permitted.

HOLOCENE PERIOD

The Holocene period began about 8,000 B.C. after the final retreat of the ice, and is marked partly by the growth of forests over formerly glaciated areas. Pollen grain study has shown that a succession of trees were dominant as the climate changed progressively. The sea-level rose gradually, and Great Britain became cut off from the continent of Europe at approximately 6,000 B.C. Climates became warmer and more like those of the present day, and the civilization of man progressed steadily.

V

How to Collect Fossils and Where to Look

Knowing where to look for fossils is the most important part of the game. You need to recognize the common sedimentary rocks on sight, as these are the rocks likely to contain fossils.

Mines and quarries are good places to collect in, for usually there are large areas of rock exposed, several horizons have been cut through and their spoil-heaps often provide a lot of well-weathered material. Railway cuttings and embankments are also good collecting grounds in some areas, for here, too, a good range of weathered-out fossils may be obtained. It is very important, however, before collecting from these and other privately owned land, to obtain permission from the owner or authority concerned. You may run into danger if you do not, as the quarry or cutting may not be safe. Road cuttings, cliffs, screes, stream and river sections are also good, and one should look out for new land excavations.

If one collects from screes and spoil-heaps, the fossils obtained may be from several different horizons. If possible, it is therefore advisable to look for fossils *in situ* in undisturbed rock, for this is the only way of knowing to which horizon or fauna the various fossils belong. One suggested method of collecting is to collect along a horizontal plane, starting at the bottom of the slope or exposure, and labelling the fossils you collect there as coming from one particular horizon. One then moves on to the higher beds, measuring the footage as breaks in the formation occur, and making separate collections from each division, labelling them carefully and precisely, so that afterwards, each fauna can be accurately determined. By these means a chronology or time scale for the entire outcrop may be established if there is sufficient material.

The best rocks in this country for both numbers of specimens and ease of collection are the Mesozoic and Tertiary limestones and clays. Many Palaeozoic horizons are excellent also, especially some of the Silurian and Carboniferous limestones and shales. Non-marine deposits do not contain good fossils as a rule, apart from the exceptional horizons which have reptile, mammal and plant remains.

A good idea is to visit your local or regional museum or university, and one of the resident staff might suggest good collecting localities. At the same time you should examine the museum's collections and particularly note the fossil faunas and the rock types of your area. Specimens on display might also suggest good collecting localities. Later you can compare your specimens with theirs.

Useful Equipment to take when Collecting

(1) Topographical Maps. These will show you the ground contours, will often mark quarry and mine sites and will generally enable you to pinpoint your localities more accurately and give them a grid reference. Ordnance Survey one-inch maps should be adequate for this, and can be obtained from most large bookshops. There is a key sheet for you to find the number of the map you require, and if they are not in stock they can always be ordered.

(2) A Geological Guide to the area you are interested in will be very useful. The Geological Survey regional guides usually contain illustrations of common fossils, mention fossiliferous horizons and give a general account of the geology of the area. They may be obtained from the Geological Survey Museum, London, S.W.7 and from H.M. Stationery Offices.

(3) Tools. A geological hammer and a chisel are essential, although any medium-sized hammer would do as a temporary makeshift. Chisels of various widths can be obtained from any toolshop, but geological hammers are more difficult to come by. Cutrock Engineering Co. Ltd., 35 Ballards Lane, London, N.3, produce geological hammers ranging from ¼ lb. to 4 lb. in weight. For general purposes the 2–lb. one is recommended, but the smaller ones are useful for extracting and trimming more delicate specimens. A hand lens is also very useful for the examination of small specimens.

(4) Paper or cloth bags of various sizes are most important for carrying the collections you make. Cloth bags are preferable and can easily be made from old scraps of material, with a drawstring around the top. Be sure to have a small note-pad and pencil with you so that you can put a label in with each bag of fossils. The label should state the exact locality with grid reference if possible, the exact horizon and a reference number (which should tie up with any notes you may have made in the field). Newspapers and very large bags should be taken for extra large specimens which need careful handling. Cotton-wool, Kleenex tissues and a few small boxes will also be useful for small fragile specimens, which should be wrapped and packed individually and carefully while still in the field.

(5) A rucksack with numerous pockets and compartments is useful as the fossils can be separated and packed more easily so

that the large heavy specimens do not break the more fragile ones.

Going into the Field

Now armed with collecting equipment and with some idea of the local geology, you can collect wherever there are suitable exposures of limestone, sandstone or shale. Different rocks require different techniques for the extraction of the fossils they contain. For instance, while collecting in soft shales it is advisable to clear away the top weathered material and then split off layers by hammering or chiselling along the bedding planes. Good slabs of fossils may be obtained in this way. In compact thickly bedded sandstones and limestones, however, often the only way to obtain fossils is to hammer off larger pieces of rock at right angles to the bedding, hoping that the rock will break away from the fossils. These pieces can then be further broken down by hammering.

Good fossils may be found in slate, but often the preservation is poor and identification made difficult by distortion. Fossils in quartzite may also be deformed, and in many sandstones only a mould of the fossil may remain. The best specimens are generally those that weather free from a shale bed or limestone.

HOME PREPARATION AND DISPLAY OF FOSSILS

From the field you can bring home large pieces of fossiliferous rock or untrimmed specimens; these can then be broken up and carefully examined at your leisure. The removal of fossils from their matrix is a great art, and several different techniques are required. For large or robust specimens in a hard rock, compact limestone, for example, hammer and chisel are needed for extraction, or even a small electric rotary drill. Trimming can then be done with a smaller hammer or a pointed needle which should be stuck in a wooden handle for ease of use. If the work is delicate it should be done under a binocular microscope or a magnifying glass, and if a large piece of rock contains several specimens which cannot be extracted, these can be ringed with ink or pencil for further examination.

To extract small fossils such as ostracods or foraminifera from clays, the rock can be broken into small pieces and boiled up in a water-filled vessel. The resultant sludge is then sieved in a fine-meshed sieve, or continuously decanted until only a coarser residue remains. The fossils can then be gently lifted out on the end of a moistened paint brush.

If the fossils are chitinous or phosphatic then weak acetic acid can be used to break away the matrix. In a few limestones the fossils have been silicified (calcified specimens can be easily scratched with a penknife, and silicified ones cannot as they are harder; on no account must calcified specimens be placed in acid, as their surface detail is soon destroyed), and these also can be dissolved out by immersion in dilute (25 per cent) acetic acid, preferably in a glass container. Be sure to first label the container with full details of the specimen. If possible the specimens should be lowered into the acid on a removable tray or basket to reduce chance of damage during removal. The acid should be renewed after forty-eight hours or so, and the specimens occasionally washed to remove loose sediment. When all the matrix has been dissolved away the fossils should be carefully washed and left to dry.

Extracted or weathered fossils and rock specimens should be cleaned as far as possible before being incorporated in a collection. Large well-preserved specimens may be scrubbed in water with a stiff brush, and a wire brush is often useful for removing vegetation or for cleaning pyritized and some silicified specimens. For more fragile fossils toothbrushes of various hardnesses are very useful. Some fossils, especially those in shale, will crumble if placed in water, and these should be carefully 'dry-cleaned' with a brush or instrument.

If while collecting or cleaning a fossil it should break, it is often possible to glue it together again successfully with a good strong gum. Fragile specimens may be varnished or strengthened by soaking in a gelatine or resinous solution and drying, or by application of the solution with a brush. If there is merely a cavity in the rock where the fossil has been dissolved away, a cast of the original fossil may be obtained by pouring or pressing melted polyvinyl chloride, or plasticene into the cavity.

Sometimes it is necessary to photograph fossils, either for study purposes or for a permanent record. Often the best results are obtained if the fossils are coated with a thin white film of ammonium chloride or magnesium oxide; these give a uniform surface and bring out the detail. The coating should be washed off after the photograph has been taken. The ammonium chloride is heated in a tube which has a bulb near one end, and is then gently blown over the fossil. The easiest way to obtain a coating of magnesium oxide is to light a piece of magnesium ribbon and carefully hold the fossil above the smoke. Practice is needed to get a good even coating.

If one wants to study the internal features of fossils such as brachiopods or corals, serial sections and cellulose peels are useful. The specimen should be mounted in a plaster block in an upright position, and then gradually ground away, a fraction at a time, either on a grinding machine or manually on a grinding plate. As the internal features appear (if cellulose peels are not to be taken, the structures of calcite specimens show up better if the fossil is heated to red heat and allowed to cool before mounting) they can be drawn or photographed at regular, measured and noted intervals, or be recorded on cellulose peels. These are made by etching the ground surface with dilute hydrochloric acid for a number of seconds, pouring acetone on the surface and then quickly pressing down a piece of celluloid or xylonite. This is attacked by the acetone and records the minutely detailed structure of the shell; it is left to dry for five to fifteen minutes on the fossil, then removed and mounted between two glass slides for examination under a microscope.

You have now collected your material, cleaned it to all intent, and are ready to sort it out in preparation to identifying it and incorporating it in your collection. During field collecting, and even when cleaning the specimens, some will look alike, and it is best to sort them all out in cardboard trays so that identification can be made first by phyla, then by class and order, and finally, if possible, by family, genera and species. Large flat boxes or lids make good sorting trays, and once the bulk of the collection has been sorted, the various genera can be placed in smaller boxes.

For displaying or storing your collection you will need a large number of boxes of all shapes and sizes. These can be made to look tidier and more uniform if you cover them with coloured or plain gummed paper. The more fragile specimens can be placed in glass-covered trays, perhaps divided into smaller compartments. You will also need a number of labels, preferably of a fairly uniform design, and preferably of stout paper or thin card. A label should be included in each box, giving the name of the fossil, the system and horizon from which it was collected, a detailed locality and a catalogue number. The number can be written on the fossil in black ink on a small patch of white enamel paint. Care should be taken to paint on an unimportant part of the specimen. The locality should, if possible, include an Ordnance Survey grid reference, which you can work out from an Ordnance Survey one-inch map.

Many collectors catalogue their specimens either in a large book or by an index card file. Each specimen then has a numbered

```
┌─────────────────────────────────────────────┐
│         Cardita senilis (Lamarck).           │
│  Coralline Crag, U.Pliocene (Astian).        │
│  Sudbourne Park, 2 miles N.W. of Orford,     │
│  Suffolk. O.S. Grid Ref. TM/466514.          │
│            Cat. No. Pl.297.                   │
└─────────────────────────────────────────────┘
```

Fig. 83. A specimen label

card with all the relevant information written on it. If publications have been consulted during identification, the title, author, date of publication, page and illustration numbers for each reference may be added to the card. The cards can then be grouped and numbered either by phyla or by stratigraphical systems.

(NOTE: Rare or problematical specimens only may be sent for comment or identification to either the Department of Palaeontology, British Museum (Natural History), Cromwell Road, London, S.W.7, or to the Geological Muscum, Exhibition Road, London, S.W.7. It is useless to send specimens if you cannot give their exact horizon and locality.)

VI

Collecting Localities

In the British Isles, fossil collectors are very fortunate to have almost every post-Pre-Cambrian formation exposed and easily accessible within such a comparatively small area. Knowing where to collect is the key to successful collecting, and the following section gives an outline of the fossiliferous horizons to be found in each county. It is not possible to give numerous detailed localities in a list of this size, and supplementary information may be obtained from books on local geology and from the Palaeontographical Society's book, *Directory of British Fossiliferous Localities*. Unfortunately this book is now out of print, but you may be able to borrow a library copy.

ENGLAND

BEDFORDSHIRE: The whole of Bedfordshire is underlain by Mesozoic rocks, but there are few accessible localities. Good Cretaceous faunas of ammonites, lamellibranchs, gastropods, brachiopods, echinoids, etc., can be collected from several pits and quarries near Leighton Buzzard.

BERKSHIRE: Several Mesozoic and Tertiary horizons outcrop in this county. Jurassic ammonites, brachiopods, lamellibranchs, echinoids, etc., can be found in several places including Marcham, Cumnor and Cothill. At Faringdon are the highly fossiliferous Cretaceous sponge-gravels, with abundant sponges, bryozoa, brachiopods, echinoids and lamellibranchs.

BUCKINGHAMSHIRE: In this county also there are many out-crops of Mesozoic and Tertiary rocks, but comparatively few good fossil localities. However, many Jurassic fossils can be collected near Aylesbury, Boarstall, Westcott and Charndon, and in pits at Marlow and Latimer good Cretaceous Upper Chalk faunas occur, with ammonites, echinoids, sponges, etc.

CAMBRIDGESHIRE: At Elsworth and Wicken there are a few Jurassic fossiliferous rocks exposed in pits and stream sections. The Upper Chalk is exposed at Wood Ditton and Weston Colville near Newmarket, and echinoids, ammonites, gastropods, etc., can be collected.

CHESHIRE: This county has few localities. Near Astbury and Dukinfield, goniatites, brachiopods, nautiloids, fish, etc., can be found in Carboniferous Coal Measures, and at Neston, non-marine lamellibranchs of the same age can be collected from old colliery tips. The only other localities are in the Triassic sand-stones of the Wirral, at Higher Bebbington and Thurstaston, where saurian footprints and plant remains are exposed from time to time.

CORNWALL: The Devonian and Carboniferous rocks of Corn-wall are not very fossiliferous. At Bude, fish and arthropods have been found in nodules in the Carboniferous Culm Measures exposed in the cliffs. At Crackington Haven goniatites and lamelli-branchs can be found in coast sections of the Culm.

CUMBERLAND: Many fossiliferous localities occur in this county, largely in Palaeozoic rocks. Ordovician slates with graptolites and occasional crustaceans outcrop at Bassenthwaite Halls near Cockermouth, and also at several localities near Keswick. There are many richly fossiliferous exposures of Carboniferous Limestone in quarries and sections near Cleator, Frizington, Hensingham, Kirkland and several other places, where the usual fauna of corals, brachiopods, lamellibranchs, trilobites and occasional fish teeth can be found. At Bigrigg, goniatites, lamellibranchs, corals and giant productids (brachiopods) can be found in the spoil heaps of old open-cast workings.

DERBYSHIRE: Carboniferous fossils are very common locally, and good localities occur near Castleton and at the base of Mam Tor, river sections near Edale, and at Bradwell, Matlock, Thorpe, Stony Middleton and numerous other places. Goniatites, corals and brachiopods are especially abundant. Goniatites are also found in exposures of Millstone Grit at Bamford, Castleton, Burbage and Hope. Pleistocene deposits with flint implements and mammal bones have been found in caves near Creswell.

DEVONSHIRE: Many fossiliferous localities can be found in this county. Faunas of Devonian corals, brachiopods, molluscs, crinoids, etc., can be found along the coast and in quarries at Combe Martin, Braunton, Croyde, Fremington, Lynton, etc., and the best coral localities occur near Torquay. Lower Carboniferous plants, fish remains, corals and brachiopods can be found near Bideford, Bishop's Tawton, Westleigh and Fremington. Abundant Cretaceous fossils including echinoids, brachiopods, bryozoa, etc., can be collected near Branscombe, Seaton, Wilmington, Beer and many other places.

DORSET: This county is also rich in fossil localities, especially along its coastline. Abundant Jurassic fossils of most kinds can be collected along the coast between Lyme Regis and Bridport, and also farther east at Abbotsbury, Osmington, Worth Matravers and Swanage. Other good localities occur around Beaminster and Sherborne. Many Cretaceous ammonites, echinoids and lamellibranchs can be found at Bincombe, Charmouth, Lulworth Cove, Swanage and elsewhere. At Southwell near Portland, Pleistocene marine shells and land snails are found associated with a raised beach.

DURHAM: Durham is underlain largely by Carboniferous and Permo-Trias. The Carboniferous Coal Measures yield non-marine lamellibranchs, including *Anthraconauta* and *Carbonicola*, and plants such as *Neuropteris*, at Durham, Castletown and Offerton, where exposures are largely in river sections. Permian limestones are exposed at several places around Sunderland and Marsden, and reef faunas (often dwarfed) of brachiopods (productids and spirifers), molluscs, nautiloids and fish can be found.

ESSEX: The Cretaceous outcrops in the north of the county, and Chalk fossils such as belemnites, echinoids and crinoids can be found at Great Chesterford and Ballingdon near Sudbury. The Tertiary and Quaternary rocks which cover the rest of the county are exposed in coastal sections near Walton-on-the-Naze, where the Red Crag yields gastropods, lamellibranchs and derived fossils such as bones and sharks' teeth.

GLOUCESTERSHIRE: This county is very rich in fossiliferous localities, especially perhaps in the Cotswolds regions. Near Halmore and Mobley, small brachiopods, and trilobite fragments can be found in exposures of Tremadocian rock. Fossiliferous Silurian rocks outcrop near Purton, Woodford and Whitfield, where quite large numbers of brachiopods, trilobites and occasional corals and ostracods may be found.

The Carboniferous Limestone is exposed in the Mendips and Bristol area, and the usual fauna of brachiopods, corals, gastropods, goniatites, algae, etc., may be collected near Chipping Sodbury, Wick, Tytherington, Henbury, Shirehampton, and many other places. Coal Measure plants can be found in workings near Warmley, and Upper Old Red Sandstone fish fragments in an old quarry near Stoke Bishop. At Westbury-on-Severn the Rhaetic Bone Bed and overlying shales are exposed, and fish teeth, bone fragments, lamellibranchs and ostracods occur. Innumerable Jurassic fossiliferous localities may be found in the Cotswolds, near Birdlip, Bishop's Cleeve, Burleigh, Cheltenham, Haresfield, Painswick, Rodborough and Upper Slaughter to mention but a few areas. There are vast numbers of the usual shelly fossils, especially brachiopods (rhynchonellids and terebratulids), corals and lamellibranchs, and also occasional reptile remains.

HAMPSHIRE: This county is underlain largely by Cretaceous, Eocene and Oligocene rocks. Cretaceous rocks are exposed in road sections and pits near Blackmoor, Chawton, Kingsclere, Odiham and Winchester; Chalk sea urchins, lamellibranchs, crinoids, brachiopods and belemnites are common. Cliff sections are usually good, for example, near Barton-on-Sea, where very many fossils can be collected from the Eocene Barton Beds. Eocene plants, forams, gastropods and lamellibranchs may also be found near Southbourne, Lee-on-Solent, Fareham, Bournemouth and Basingstoke. On the coast at Milford-on-Sea, Oligocene plants, shells and vertebrate remains occur.

HEREFORDSHIRE: This county has several good Silurian localities, and at Downton-on-the-Rock a number of horizons are exposed in a river section where many brachiopods may be collected. At Fownhope, Leintwardine, Mochtree, Mordiford, Nash and Woolhope, Silurian limestones and shales often yield rich faunas of corals, trilobites, brachiopods, crinoids, etc., and at Perton, Kington, Suckley and several other localities, Upper Silurian plant and fish remains, and rare molluscs and ostracods are found. A few fish remains have been found also in Devonian sandstones near Clodock, Kentchurch and Newton.

HERTFORDSHIRE: There are not a great number of good localities. Numerous Chalk pits yielding the usual faunas can be found, and in a few pits around Hitchin rare ammonoid faunas can be collected from the Chalk Rock.

HUNTINGDONSHIRE: This county is underlain largely by Jurassic rocks, but there are few good localities. At Warboys the Oxford Clay (Jurassic) is exposed in a clay pit, and abundant pyritized ammonites, gastropods, lamellibranchs, brachiopods, etc., can be collected.

ISLE OF MAN: Several good Carboniferous Limestone exposures occur at Balladoole, Ballasalla, Castletown and Derbyhaven (nearly all coastal exposures), and abundant corals, bryozoa, brachiopods, molluscs, crinoids and plants can usually be collected.

ISLE OF WIGHT: The Isle of Wight has excellent coast sections of Tertiary and Cretaceous rocks. At Bonchurch, Brighstone, the cliffs of the Freshwater area, Niton, Sandown, Shanklin and

Alum Bay, good Cretaceous faunas of ammonites, sea urchins, molluscs and plants can be collected. In Whitecliff Bay and Alum Bay are the finest Tertiary sections in England, with many Eocene and Oligocene horizons exposed, and yielding large faunas of lamellibranchs, forams, corals, bryozoa and fresh-water shells. At Cowes, Totland, Yarmouth and Freshwater, Oligocene and Eocene exposures yield rich faunas, including insects, foraminifers, fresh-water gastropods, etc.

KENT: Some coastal sections are quite fossiliferous. At Folkestone, St. Margaret's Bay, Walmer, Margate and Ramsgate, several Cretaceous horizons yield Chalk and Gault faunas, and Pleistocene non-marine shells have been found on the cliff-tops at Folkestone. Other good Cretaceous localities occur at Cliffe, Ditton, Ightham, Maidstone, Postling, Sittingbourne, Swanscombe and Tilmanstone and several pits in the Medway Valley. At Abbey Wood, Eocene gastropods, lamellibranchs and mammal, reptile and fish remains may be collected, and also at High Halstow, Minster in Sheppey, Upnor, Newington, Ramsgate and Herne Bay. Pleistocene bones and artifacts occur in gravel pits at Swanscombe.

LANCASHIRE: Most fossiliferous localities in this county are of Carboniferous age, but at Ashgill Beck near Coniston, many Ordovician trilobites may be collected. The usual shelly Carboniferous Limestone fossils can be found in quarries and cliffs near and around Clitheroe, Dalton-in-Furness, Grange and Stainton, and Millstone Grit goniatites in river sections near Wiswell and Samlesbury. Coal Measure non-marine shells, goniatites and plants occur in workings and sections near Wigan, Upholland and Whiston. Permian lamellibranchs occur in a stream section near Bispham, and Triassic plants and footprints occur in sand-stones in small quarries and exposures in and around Liverpool and also at Lymm.

LEICESTERSHIRE: Carboniferous Limestone brachiopods and corals can be collected in quarries at Worthington and Breedon-on-the-Hill, and Lower Jurassic faunas of ammonites, brachio-pods, lamellibranchs, corals, etc., from quarries and cuttings near Braunston, Old Dalby, Scalford, Sproxton and Waltham-on-the-Wolds.

LINCOLNSHIRE: This county is very good for Mesozoic fossils, and abundant Jurassic fossils can be collected from numerous quarries. Some of the best localities include those near Ancaster, Appleby, Bracebridge, Castle Bytham, Denton, Greetwell, Scun-thorpe, Sleaford and Stickney, where the usual ammonites, brachiopods, lamellibranchs, corals, etc., are abundant. Chalk sea urchins, brachiopods, belemnites, etc., and Gault brachiopods and rare ammonites can be found at South Ferriby, and at Nettleton, fairly abundant Lower Cretaceous ammonites, lamellibranchs, etc., can be collected in old workings. At Broughton, a Holocene tufa contains numerous non-marine mollusca.

LONDON AND MIDDLESEX: This area offers little to the fossil collector, and the only good localities now are the pits at Hare-field and at Charlton, at both of which places Lower Tertiary faunas may be found.

MONMOUTHSHIRE: This county is largely underlain by Old Red Sandstone and Carboniferous, and has few fossiliferous localities of note. The odd Coal Measure fossils can be found in the valleys of the north-western part of the county, and Upper Silurian rocks outcrop in the Usk inlier. At Bishopston, near Newport, lamellibranchs can be collected from Rhaetic shales.

NORFOLK: Rich Cretaceous faunas can be collected from several Chalk pits in and around Norwich, cuttings near Swaffham and beach exposures near Trimingham and Old Hunstanton. At Bramerton, Pleistocene marine molluscs, and at West Runton Early Pleistocene mammal remains and plant seeds and fruit may be found.

NORTHAMPTONSHIRE: The fossils to be collected in this county are mostly of Lower and Middle Jurassic age. Large numbers of brachiopods, ammonites, lamellibranchs, gastropods and occasional belemnites can be found in pits and quarries near Brixworth, Collyweston, Desborough, Geddington, Great Weldon, Gretton, Kettering, King's Sutton, Thrapston and several other places.

NORTHUMBERLAND: This county has many Carboniferous localities. The usual faunas of shelly Carboniferous Limestone can be collected along coast sections near Bamburgh, Beadnall, Berwick-on-Tweed, Howick and Scremerston, and from quarries and streams near Hartburn, Hepple, Rothbury and numerous other places. Coal Measure non-marine shells can be found on the coast near Hartley and in Whitley Bay.

NOTTINGHAMSHIRE: There are not many good fossiliferous localities in this county. Rhaetic lamellibranchs may be collected near Bunny and in a clay pit at Cropwell Bishop. Lower Jurassic ammonites and occasional reptiles and fish have been found in quarries at Barnstone.

Collecting Localities

OXFORDSHIRE: There are many good Mesozoic localities. Quite a large number of quarries in the Oxford area yield large Upper Jurassic faunas of ammonites, oysters, brachiopods, corals, gastropods and occasional bones, for instance at Beckley, Islip, Kirtlington and Littlemore. Many Jurassic fossils can also be found in quarries at Ardley, Bladon, Chipping Norton, Hook Norton, Sarsden and Whitney. Cretaceous exposures at Culham and at Emmer Green near Reading yield echinoids, ammonites, etc.

RUTLAND: This small county has few localities, but Jurassic lamellibranchs, brachiopods, corals and gastropods may be collected from quarries near Clipsham and Ketton.

SHROPSHIRE: This county has a large number of good Lower Palaeozoic localities. Lower Cambrian brachiopods and hyolithids can be collected from All Stretton quarry near Church Stretton, and trilobite fragments from a stream section at Comley. Middle Cambrian trilobites, brachiopods and dendroid graptolites are found at Comley, Eaton Consterdine and Shineton. Ordovician trilobites, brachiopods and sometimes graptolites occur at Brockton, Bromlow, Cheney Longville, Pennerley and Snailbeach. In the Onny River section near Wistantow, many trinucleid trilobites are found, and another good trilobite locality occurs near Hope. In an Ordovician section at Shelve, graptolites and cystid plates can be collected.

Shelly Silurian faunas of trilobites, corals, brachiopods, etc., can be seen at Cleobury Mortimer, Hughley, Hungerford, Leighton, Onibury, Plowden and Shelve. Numerous quarries along Wenlock Edge yield abundant shelly faunas of corals, stromatoporoids, brachiopods, crinoids, etc., and graptolites can be collected near Chirbury, Middletown and Little Wenlock.

Carboniferous brachiopods, fish teeth and spines are to be found in quarries at Farlow, and also Upper Old Red Sandstone fish.

SOMERSET: This is also a very good county for both Palaeozoic and Mesozoic fossils. Silurian shelly fossils can be collected from a field at Leigh-upon-Mendip, and Devonian corals, brachiopods, plants, etc., from Holford, Timberscombe, Wheddon Cross and several other places. The usual prolific Carboniferous Limestone faunas of corals and brachiopods can be collected at quarries in numerous places, including Backwell, Binegar, Burrington, Cleeve, Dulcote, Failand, Long Ashton and Wrington. At some places, for example, Portishead and Waterlip, silicified specimens occur, which can be dissolved out in acid. Millstone Grit goniatites can be found in a quarry at Winford, and Coal Measure plants on tip heaps at Camerton and Midsomer Norton. Triassic lamellibranchs and fish remains can be seen on the shore at Blue Anchor.

There are many Jurassic fossiliferous localities in the eastern part of the county, and some of the best are those in exposures and quarries near Chesterblade, Corton Denham, Dundry, Dunkerton, Keynsham, Maperton, Marston Magna, Midford, Shepton Beauchamp and Welton. Pleistocene bones and antlers have been found in gravel pits near Bleadon and Tiverton (over the border).

STAFFORDSHIRE: Highly fossiliferous Silurian Wenlock Limestone and Shales outcrop in various exposures and quarries around Dudley and west of Great Barr, and very rich faunas of corals, trilobites, brachiopods stromatoporoids, etc., can be collected. Upper Silurian shales occur at Netherton, and yield fish remains and brachiopods. At Caulden, sparsely fossiliferous

Carboniferous Limestone outcrops, but at Waterfall, Water-houses and Wootton abundant fossils of the same age can be collected. Millstone Grit goniatites and lamellibranchs are found at Brindley Ford and Meerbrook, and Coal Measure molluscs at Gillow Heath, Kingsley and Biddulph, largely on old tip heaps. Coal Measure plants are also found near Newcastle-under-Lyme.

SUFFOLK: Largely Quaternary fossils are found in this county, but Cretaceous belemnites, sea urchins, corals, brachiopods, crinoids, etc., are found near Bramford, Claydon and Sudbury. Pliocene Coralline Crag, with abundant lamellibranchs, gastropods, bryozoa, forams and occasional sea urchins and crabs, outcrops in pits near Aldeburgh, Orford and Sudbourne. Red Crag, with numerous lamellibranchs, gastropods and derived mammal bones, fish teeth and bryozoa, occurs at Bawdsey, Hollesley, Newbourne and Ramsholt. Pleistocene gravels at Stutton yield mammal bones and fresh-water molluscs.

SURREY: The best fossiliferous localities of this county are of Cretaceous age. Large faunas of sea urchins, lamellibranchs, starfish, sponges, ammonites, bryozoa, etc., are found in pits at Albury, Betchworth, Compton, Fareham, Godstone, Guildford and Onslow, Mickleham, Oxted, Seale and many other places.

SUSSEX: In this county also the best fossils are to be found in the Cretaceous. Chalk echinoids, oysters, belemnites, etc., can be collected in pits near Arundel, Boxgrove, Burpham, Durrington, Friston, Houghton, Lavant, Lewes, Offham, Rottingdean, Singleton and several other places; Cretaceous Greensand ammonites, lamellibranchs, etc., can be found on the shore at Eastbourne. Eocene London Clay faunas of lamellibranchs, gastropods, corals, crustaceans, fish, etc., occur on the shore at Bognor Regis, and mollusca can be found in the Woolwich Beds on the coast near Newhaven. On the shore at Selsey, Bracklesham Beds yield rich faunas of lamellibranchs, forams, gastropods, corals, vertebrates, etc.

WARWICKSHIRE: Lower Cambrian brachiopods and hyolithids have been found in a quarry at Hartshill near Nuneaton, and Carboniferous Coal Measure brachiopods, worms and non-marine lamellibranchs and gastropods can be found in old pits at Dosthill and Longford. Triassic plant remains, small crustaceans and amphibian and fish teeth and bones have been collected from a cutting near Spernal, and abundant Jurassic ammonites and other fossils from near Longford.

WESTMORLAND: This county has a number of good Palaeozoic localities. At Cautley and Salley Brow near Sedburgh, fossiliferous nodules occur in Ordovician mudstones, and Ordovician trilobites and brachiopods may be collected near Kentmere and Troutbeck. Abundant Silurian graptolites have been found at various localities near Ambleside, Kentmere and Stockdale, and at Cautley, trilobites also. Highly fossiliferous Carboniferous Limestone provides good collecting in quarries and stream sections near Birkdale, Crosby Ravensworth, Kaber, Kirkby Stephen, Shap, Raisbeck and many other places. Lower Carboniferous brachiopods and corals of the Yoredale Series can be collected at Dufton, Great Strickland, Hackthorpe and Tirril. In the neighbourhood of Appleby, certain Permo-Trias horizons yield plant remains.

WILTSHIRE: This county offers largely Mesozoic localities.

Many Jurassic ammonites, lamellibranchs, brachiopods, corals, ostracods, etc., can be collected in quarries and exposures near Bradford-on-Avon, Calne, Charlton and Garsden, Heywood, Malmesbury, Purton, Seend, Stanton St. Quintin, Steeple Ashton and Swindon. Cretaceous fossils are also plentiful locally, and Chalk faunas are found in pits at Alderbury, Downton, Fyfield, Marlborough, Oare, Pitton and Woodford. Gault ammonites can be collected in a brickyard in Devizes.

WORCESTERSHIRE: Not many fossiliferous localities occur in this county on the whole. Silurian graptolites can be found in a quarry near Great Whitley, and Upper Silurian lamellibranchs and fish fragments in a stream section near Shatterford. In quarries at Bromsgrove rare plants and arthropods have been found in Triassic sandstones.

YORKSHIRE (WEST RIDING): Most of the localities are of Carboniferous age, but Ordovician and Silurian trilobites and brachiopods are found at a number of localities near Austwick and Sedburgh. The rich Carboniferous Limestone faunas of brachiopods, corals, algae, and occasional goniatites and trilobites can be collected at numerous quarries, cliffs and natural exposures at Airton, Cracoe, Giggleswick, Horton-in-Ribblesdale, Greenhow, Ingleton, Malham, Newton-in-Bowland, Settle and Skipton. Corals and brachiopods of the Yoredale Series are found at Feizor, Lofthouse and Settle, and Millstone Grit goniatites and lamellibranchs near Blubberhouses, Cowling, Keighley, Marsden, Todmorden and other places. Coal Measure goniatites and non-marine lamellibranchs can be collected at Baildon, Bolton-upon-Dearne, Bradgate, Horsforth and Rotherham, and Permian lamellibranchs, brachiopods and bryozoa in quarries at Hampole.

Pleistocene mammal bones have been found in a cave near Settle.

YORKSHIRE (NORTH RIDING): In this riding the fossiliferous exposures are largely of Carboniferous and Jurassic age. Lower Carboniferous shelly faunas are found at Askrigg, Aysgarth, Hawes and Leyburn, and Upper Carboniferous corals and molluscs at Arkengarthdale. Abundant Jurassic ammonites, corals, gastropods, lamellibranchs, brachiopods, etc., can be collected from good coastal sections near Ravenscar, Robin Hood's Bay, Whitby, Burniston, Cayton, Cloughton, Filey, Gristhorpe and Scarborough, and numerous inland quarries and exposures such as those at Pickering, Seamer, Cawton, Boltby and Ampleforth.

YORKSHIRE (EAST RIDING): All localities in this riding are of Mesozoic age. Good Jurassic ammonites, lamellibranchs, corals, etc., can be collected from Hotham, North Grimston, and South Cave, and Chalk fossils are found in numerous pits near Bessingby, Beverley, Burdale, Flamborough, Market Weighton, Ruston Parva, Speeton, Willerby and many other places.

WALES

ANGLESEY: Anglesey has a number of good localities, mainly of Ordovician and Lower Carboniferous age. In the north of the island near Amlwch, Parys Mountain, Cemaes and Llanbabo are localities where Ordovician graptolites and brachiopods can be collected. Ordovician brachiopods, trilobites and graptolites are also found near Llanerchymedd, Rhosneigr, and a few places near Beaumaris and Menai Bridge. Carboniferous Limestone brachiopods, corals, gastropods, occasional trilobites and fish scales and spines can be found in quarries, cliffs and exposures at Red Wharfe Bay, Holland Arms, Llangaffo and Moelfre. At Tre-Arddur a Holocene submerged forest is visible at low tide.

BRECKNOCK: Rare Devonian ostracods have been found in a quarry at Crickhowell, and Carboniferous Millstone Grit goniatites, lamellibranchs, brachiopods and nautiloids at Abercrave and Colbren. Coal Measure plants and non-marine lamellibranchs can be collected at Ystradgynlais and at Abercrave on the banks of the River Llech.

CARDIGANSHIRE: This county has few localities, but there is a noted graptolite locality at Pont-Erwyd, along the River Rheidol. Graptolites can also be collected at Waun-Fawr near Aberystwyth.

CARMARTHENSHIRE: There are a number of good Palaeozoic fossiliferous localities. Tremadocian trilobites can be found in stream sections at Carmarthen, and abundant Ordovician graptolites near Abergwili and Whitland, and shelly and graptolitic faunas at Llandilo, Llandowror and St. Clears. Devonian fish and plants occur near Ferryside and Kidwelly, and abundant Carboniferous Limestone corals, brachiopods, bryozoa, etc., are also found at Kidwelly. Millstone Grit goniatites, lamellibranchs, crinoid stems and occasional plant remains can be collected from Garnant, Brynammon, Cwmllynfell and Llandebie, and Coal Measure plants in a stream section near Gorslas.

CARNARVONSHIRE: There are a number of fairly good but scattered outcrops of fossiliferous Lower Palaeozoic rocks. At

Bethesda, distorted Lower Cambrian trilobites are found in slates, and around Portmadoc, Upper Cambrian trilobites, brachiopods and dendroid graptolites can be collected from several localities. Ordovician graptolites are found on the shore at Bangor, in a river section at Carnarvon, and at Deganwy, Llandegai, Portmadoc and Dolwyddelan, where crinoids, brachiopods, lamellibranchs and trilobites also occur. Silurian graptolites can be found at Llangwstenin near Colwyn Bay. On the Great and Little Ormes at Llandudno and on the coast at Bangor and Deganwy, Carboniferous Limestone faunas can be collected.

DENBIGHSHIRE: This county has good Palaeozoic localities. In a road section at Glyn Ceiriog Ordovician trilobites, brachiopods and bryozoa are abundant, and numerous Silurian graptolites can be collected at quarries and sections at Clocaenog, Glan Conway, Eglwys-Fach, Gwytherin, Llanwrst and Llansannan. Carboniferous faunas are found in quarries around Denbigh, Llandulas, Ruthin and the Eglwyseg and Trevor escarpments near Llangollen. Millstone Grit goniatites and brachiopods occur near Pen-y-Cae, and Coal Measure plants on tip heaps at Brymbo, Bersham and Plas Power near Wrexham.

FLINTSHIRE: This county has largely Carboniferous localities, but Silurian brachiopods and occasional trilobites can be found on Moel Fammau near Cilcain. Rich Carboniferous Limestone faunas can be collected in quarries and exposures at Dyserth, Gwaenysgor, Halkyn, Holywell, Mold and Prestatyn, and Millstone Grit goniatites at Holywell, Halkyn and Higher Kinnerton. Coal Measure non-marine lamellibranchs can be found at Bryn Celyn, Caergwle and Gwespyr, and at Caerwys a post-glacial tufa contains land and fresh-water molluscs.

Collecting Localities

GLAMORGAN: This county has a number of localities, including some good coast sections. Highly fossiliferous Carboniferous Limestone is found at Oystermouth, Sutton and Tongwynlais, and Millstone Grit plants, goniatites and non-marine lamellibranchs at Rudry. On old tip heaps at several places, including Abercanaid, Caerphilly, Cwmtwrch, Ferndale and Ynys-Boeth, Coal Measure plants and non-marine lamellibranchs can be collected. In a quarry at Kenfig Hill there is a Triassic conglomerate containing derived Carboniferous fossils, and on the coast at Lavernock and St. Mary's Well Bay Triassic, Rhaetic and Jurassic rocks yield lamellibranchs, fish remains, ammonites and oysters. Jurassic ammonites and oysters are also found on the coast at Llantwit Major and St. Donats.

MERIONETHSHIRE: A stream section near Maentwrog yields many Cambrian trilobites, and Cambrian trilobites and brachiopods have been found in stream sections near Dolgelley. At numerous exposures in the vicinity of Arenig Station, Cambrian and Ordovician brachiopods, trilobites, molluscs and graptolites can be collected, and many Ordovician brachiopods, trilobites and graptolites are to be found in quarries and exposures near Bala, Llan Ffestiniog, Llangower and Rhydymain. Carboniferous Limestone corals and brachiopods can be collected from a quarry near Corwen.

MONTGOMERYSHIRE: There are several Ordovician localities, and shelly faunas can be found near Llanfyllin, Llangyniew, Llanyblodwel and Meifod. Silurian graptolites are found at Derwenlas, and Silurian shelly fossils in a road section near Llangyniew.

PEMBROKESHIRE: This county has numerous good fossil localities of Palaeozoic age. Cambrian brachiopods and trilobites can be collected on the shore and from quarries near Solva, St. David's and Haverfordwest, and many Ordovician graptolites may be found in quarries and exposures at Abereiddy, Bletherston, Clarbeston, Fishguard, Narberth and St. David's. Shelly Ordovician and Silurian faunas can be collected at Haverfordwest, Keeston, Narberth, Robeston Wathen, Pembroke, Tiers Cross, Castlemartin and several other places. Devonian brachiopods, lamellibranchs and fish and plant remains can be collected at Angle, Cosheston and Manorbier; abundant Carboniferous Limestone fossils at Bosherston, Castlemartin and Lydstep; Millstone Grit goniatites and lamellibranchs at Amroth, Cresswell, Gumfreston and Tenby, and Coal Measure non-marine lamellibranchs, crustacea, plants, etc., at Boulston, Little Haven and Tenby. In caves and fissures in the Carboniferous Limestone at Tenby, Pleistocene deposits with implements and mammal bones have been found, but are now mostly quarried away.

RADNORSHIRE: This county has few localities, but Ordovician and Silurian graptolites and shelly faunas can be collected in several sections and quarries near Builth Wells, Llandrindod Wells and Old Radnor.

SCOTLAND

ABERDEENSHIRE: This county offers little to the fossil collector. One famous locality is that at Dryden near Rhynie, where Middle Old Red Sandstone (Devonian) Rhynie Chert contains remains of woody plants, crustacea and the earliest insects.

ARGYLL: The mainland section of this county has few localities, but in Tirfergus Glen near Campbelltown, Lower Carboniferous plants, brachiopods, molluscs and trilobites can be collected.

ARGYLL (ARDNAMURCHAN): From coastal sections near Kilmory and Kilchoan, Lower and Middle Jurassic lamellibranchs, brachiopods, ammonites, belemnites, corals, etc., can be collected.

ARGYLL (MULL): Near Gribun, Rhaetic beds yield lamellibranchs and fish scales, and Cretaceous lamellibranchs and brachiopods can also be found there. Jurassic Liassic brachiopods, molluscs, etc., can be collected from several shore localities near Bunessan, Lochbuie and Ardmeanach.

AYRSHIRE: This county is very good for Palaeozoic fossils. Ordovician graptolites, brachiopods, molluscs, algae, etc., can be collected near Ballantrae (Bennane Head), Barr, Carsphairn, New Dailly and Girvan. Starfish Beds are exposed in Lady Burn near New Dailly. Silurian shelly fossils and occasional crustaceans and plant and fish remains can be found near Barr, Muirkirk, Girvan and New Dailly. Many Carboniferous Limestone fossils may be collected in quarries and sections at Beith, Dalblair, Dalry, Galston, Muirkirk and many other places; Millstone Grit fossils at Dalry and Kilmarnock, and Coal Measure plants and molluscs near Kilmarnock, Saltcoats, Ochiltree and Dalmellington.

BANFFSHIRE: There are few localities in this county. Middle Old Red Sandstone with well-preserved fish (crossopterygians and placoderms) have been found in a river section at Fochabers, and also at Gardenstown of Gamrie.

Collecting Localities

BERWICKSHIRE: This county has a number of good Palaeozoic localities, especially along its coast. Ordovician graptolites are found at Fala, and Silurian shelly faunas and graptolites at Cockburnspath, Spottiswoode and Westruther. Devonian fish remains can be collected at Cockburnspath and Greenlaw, and the usual abundant Lower Carboniferous faunas at Allantown, Berwick-on-Tweed, Cockburnspath, Coldstream and Lennel.

BUTESHIRE (ARRAN): Lower Carboniferous sandstones and limestones yield brachiopods, lamellibranchs, gastropods, plant and fish remains, trilobites and nautiloids in coast sections near Corrie and Lochranza.

CAITHNESS: This county is famous for its Middle Old Red Sandstone fish. These have been found in quarries and coast sections at Castletown, John o' Groats, Scrabster, Spital and Thurso.

CLACKMANNAN: There are few localities, but Carboniferous Millstone Grit crinoids, brachiopods and ostracods are found at Cambus on the banks of the River Devon, and Coal Measure plants in a stream section near Tillicoultry.

DUNBARTONSHIRE: This county also has few localities. Lower Carboniferous shelly fossils can be collected near Cumbernauld, Bowling and Kilsyth, and Millstone Grit brachiopods, lamellibranchs and plants at Cumernauld.

DUMFRIESSHIRE: This county has many Palaeozoic fossiliferous localities. Ordovician graptolites and brachiopods can be collected in stream sections and exposures at Abington, Dobb's Linn (a classic locality near Birkhill), Dunscore, Kirkconnel, Moffat,

Sanquhar and many other places. Many Silurian graptolites, brachiopods and cephalopods can be collected at Dunscore, Langholm, Lockerbie, Moffat and Raehills. Highly fossiliferous Carboniferous Limestone also outcrops at Canonbie, Ecclefechan, Langholm and Kirtle Bridge, and Coal Measure ostracods, lamellibranchs and cephalopods may be collected at Canonbie and Kirkconnel.

EAST LOTHIAN: This county has mainly Carboniferous localities, but Ordovician graptolites and brachiopods can be found in stream sections near East Salton and Garvald. Abundant Carboniferous shelly faunas may be collected from shore sections and quarries near Aberlady, Broxburn, Dunbar, Haddington, Innerwick, Pathend and Skateraw. Millstone Grit and Coal Measure plants and non-marine lamellibranchs can be found at Port Seton, and at Aberlady, recent raised beach deposits yield marine lamellibranchs, etc.

FIFESHIRE: This county has largely Carboniferous localities, but at Newburgh, Wormit Bay, Cupar and Blebocraigs, Devonian fish, eurypterid and plant remains have been found. The usual Carboniferous Limestone faunas are abundant in quarries and coastal sections at Aberdour, Culross, Dunfermline, Kirkcaldy, Largo, St. Andrews and many other places. Millstone Grit brachiopods, gastropods and lamellibranchs can be collected at Culross and Dollar, and Coal Measure non-marine lamellibranchs on the coast at Dysart and West Wemyss.

FORFARSHIRE: Fossils are scarce in this county, but occasional Lower Old Red Sandstone fish, eurypterid and plant remains are to be found in the waste heaps of old quarries near Forfar.

INVERNESS (EIGG): There are several shore exposures of Upper Jurassic rocks, where lamellibranchs, gastropods, fish, reptiles, ammonites and crustaceans can be collected.

INVERNESS (MUCK): Near Camas Mor, Upper Jurassic lamellibranchs, gastropods, ostracods and phyllopods can be collected from shore exposures.

INVERNESS (RAASAY): There are several good Lower Jurassic exposures on the island. Near Hallag, Holloman, Inverarish and Screapadal, ammonites, lamellibranchs, gastropods and belemnites are to be found.

INVERNESS (SCALPA): On the southern side of the island Jurassic ammonites, belemnites, lamellibranchs, etc., occur, and Upper Cretaceous corals, gastropods and lamellibranchs can also be collected.

INVERNESS (SKYE): Cambrian sponges, lamellibranchs, annelids, gastropods and cephalopods can be collected from the Durness Limestone near Broadford, Torran, Tokavaig and Ord. Rhaetic lamellibranchs, fish scales and plants are found at Heast and Lusa, and highly fossiliferous Jurassic rocks outcrop on the shore and in quarries near Broadford, Elgol, Holm, Kirkibost, Portree, Rigg, Torran and Strathaird.

KINCARDINESHIRE: There are a few fossiliferous localities in this county. At Stonehaven, Upper Silurian arthropods and fish remains have been collected from the shore.

KINROSS: This county also has few localities, but Carboniferous

Limestone and Millstone Grit sections are found at Dollar, and yield brachiopods, lamellibranchs and gastropods.

KIRKCUDBRIGHT: There are several good Lower Palaeozoic localities. At Castle Douglas, Dalry, New Galloway and Tynron abundant Ordovician graptolites can be collected, and Silurian graptolites at Balmaclellan, Corsock, Dunscore, Kirkcudbright, Lawrieston and Parton. Shelly Silurian faunas are found at Dundrennan, the shore at Kirkcudbright, and several other places. Lower Carboniferous shelly fossils can be collected near Arbigland and Southwick.

LANARKSHIRE: This county has many fossiliferous localities. Ordovician graptolites and brachiopods can be collected at Abington and Lamington; Silurian graptolites at Tweedsmuir, and Silurian ostracods, eurypterids and fish remains at Muirkirk. Carboniferous shelly faunas can be collected at Braidwood, Carluke, Coalburn, East Kilbride, Lanark, Lesmahagow, Stonehouse and Strathaven, and Coal Measure plants, lamellibranchs and goniatites at Avonbank, Bothwell, Dalserf, Douglas, Kennox, Larkhall and Waterloo.

MIDLOTHIAN: This county also has many Palaeozoic localities, mainly of Carboniferous age. Ordovician graptolites can be collected near Heriot, and Silurian graptolites at Stow. A Silurian shelly fauna can also be found in a stream section near Carlops. Lower Carboniferous forams, echinoids, corals, brachiopods, lamellibranchs, cephalopods, etc., can be collected from Borthwick, Colinton, Dalkeith, Edinburgh, Loanhead, Straiton and many other places, and Millstone Grit brachiopods, lamellibranchs, gastropods, etc., from sections near Polton and Gorebridge. Coal Measure plants and non-marine lamellibranchs are found near Bonnyrig and Dalkeith.

MORAYSHIRE: Devonian fossil fish have been found in Upper Old Red Sandstone at Rosebrae Quarry near Elgin, and near Longmorn Station. At Lossiemouth, rare Triassic reptile remains have been found.

NAIRNSHIRE: Devonian fossil fish have been found in quarries near the coast at Nairn.

PEEBLESSHIRE: Ordovician graptolites can be collected near Culter and Peebles, and Ordovician and Silurian shelly faunas near Broughton, Eddleston, Leadburn, Wrae, Baddingsgill and Innerleithen. Lower Carboniferous crinoids, corals, lamellibranchs and forams can be found near Carlops and West Linton.

RENFREWSHIRE: All localities in this county are in Carboniferous Limestone, and the usual faunas can be collected near Barrhead, Bridge of Weir, Howwood, Paisley and Johnstone.

ROSS AND CROMARTY: In stream sections near Achneigie and Kinlochewe, Cambrian worms, molluscs, trilobites and brachiopods can be collected, and on the shore at Cromarty numerous fish have been found in nodules in Devonian Old Red Sandstone. Jurassic plants and shelly fossils can be collected from exposures near Applecross, Ethie and Balintore.

ROXBURGHSHIRE: Silurian graptolites, arthropods and cephalopods can be collected from several exposures near Edgerston, Hownam, Riccarton, Stobs Castle and Wolflee. Abundant Lower

Carboniferous fossils can be found in quarries and exposures near Langholm, Newcastleton, Penton and Riccarton.

SELKIRKSHIRE: Ordovician brachiopods and graptolites can be collected from Chapelhope, Ettrickbridgend, Melrose and Yarrow, and good Silurian graptolites from exposures near Clovenfords, Galashiels, Kirkhope and Melrose.

STIRLINGSHIRE: This county has only Carboniferous localities. Prolific Lower Carboniferous faunas are found in quarries and river sections at Baldow, Denny, Kilsyth, Lennoxtown, Linlithgow, and Murrayshall. Millstone Grit brachiopods, gastropods and lamellibranchs can be collected from a stream section near Larbert.

SUTHERLANDSHIRE: Cambrian brachiopods, gastropods, cephalopods, sponges and worms are found near Durness and Heilem, and abundant and varied Jurassic faunas can be collected in cuttings and shore exposures near Brora, Clyneleish, Golspie, Helmsdale, Kintradwell and Wester Garty.

WEST LOTHIAN: This county has a few Lower Carboniferous localities, and brachiopods, lamellibranchs, corals, annelids, plant and fish remains can be collected at Bathgate, Dalmeny and Linlithgow.

WIGTOWNSHIRE: This county has several Palaeozoic exposures. Ordovician or Silurian graptolites can be collected at many localities near Colfin, Kirkcolm, Kirkcowan, Port Patrick, Mochrum, Stranraer, Wigtown, Glenluce, Stoneykirk, Whithorn and other places. Carboniferous Coal Measure plants occur at Kirkcolm, and near Stranraer, Pleistocene glacial deposits contain lamellibranchs, foraminifers and gastropods.

133

Further Reading

OUTLINES OF GEOLOGY

AGER, D. V., *Introducing Geology* (Faber & Faber), 1960.

EVANS, I. O., *Observer's Book of British Geology* (F. Warne), London, 1949.

FEARNSIDES, W. G. and BULMAN, O. M. B., *Geology in the Service of Man* (Pelican Books), London, 1953.

HOLMES, A., *Principles of Physical Geology* (Nelson), London, 1948.

READ, H. H., *Geology: an Introduction to Earth History* (Home University Library), 1953.

SEWARD, A. C., *Geology for Everyman* (Cambridge University Press), 1943.

PALAEONTOLOGY AND FOSSIL COLLECTING

DAVIES, A. M., *An Introduction to Palaeontology* (Murby), London, 1947.

KNIGHT, C. R., *Life through the Ages* (New York), 1946.

OAKLEY, K. P. and MUIRWOOD, H. M., *The Succession of Life through Geological Time* (British Museum Natural History Publications), 1956. (Obtainable from the British Museum (Natural History) and from H.M. Stationery Offices)

ROMER, A. S., *Man and the Vertebrates* (Pelican Books), London, 1954.

Further Reading

Swinnerton, H. H., *Outlines of Palaeontology* (Arnold), London, 1947.

Swinton, W. E., *The Corridor of Life* (Cape), London, 1948.

Walton, J., *Introduction to the Study of Fossil Plants* (Blackie), London, 1953.

Woods, H., *Palaeontology, Invertebrate* (Cambridge University Press), 1946.

Other useful books are the *Instructions for Collectors, No. 11; Fossils, Minerals and Rocks,* and *British Fossils* (in three volumes) which is shortly to be published. Both these are produced by the British Museum Natural History Publications, and are or will be available from the British Museum (Natural History) and H.M. Stationery Offices.

GEOLOGY OF THE BRITISH ISLES

Geological Survey, *Handbooks to the Regional Geology of Great Britain* (eighteen parts) (Stationery Office), London. Obtainable from the Geological Survey and Museum and from H.M. Stationery Offices.

Geologists' Association, *Geologists' Association Guides*. A series of geological guides to specific areas. Obtainable from Benham and Company Ltd., 12 Culver Street, Colchester.

Stamp, L. D., *An Introduction to Stratigraphy* (Murby), London, 1934; 'Britain's Structure and Scenery' (*New Naturalist*) (Collins), London, 1946.

Wells, A. K. and Kircaldy, J. F., *Outline of Historical Geology* (Allen & Unwin), London, 1958.

Wills, L. J., *A Palaeographical Atlas of Great Britain and adjacent parts of Europe* (Blackie), London, 1959.

Index

Index

Index

King Crab, *see Limulus*, 41
Karroo Sandstone, 82
Labyrinthodonts, 53
Lamellibranchs, 41–2, 86, 93
Latimeria, 87
Lehmann, Johann Gottlob, 17
Leidy, Joseph, 19
Leonardo da Vinci, 15
Leopard, 93
Lepidocyclina, 91, 93
Lepidodendron, 61, 77, 80
Lichens, 59
Limpets, 41
Limulus, 41
Lion, 98
Lion cats, 93
Lister, Martin, 17
Liverworts, 60
Lobsters, 86
Lonsdaleia floriformis, 32
Ludlow Bone Bed, 50
Lung fish, 51
Lycopodiales, 61
Lyell, Sir Charles, 20

Macropoma, 87
Maidenhair tree, 85
Mammals, 53, 56–7, 80, 82, 85, 87, 89, 91, 94
Mammoths, 98
Maps, 101
Marsupials, 87
Marsupites, 47
Megalosaurus, 84
Merostomata, 40
Mesohippus, 91
Mesozoic era, 65, 80 ff.
Metamorphic rock, 64

Methane gas proportionate method, 64
Micraster, 48, 93
Millstone Grit, 76
Mineralization, 23
Miocene period, 92–3
Mites, 74
Moa, 98
Molluscs, classification of, 41–4
    fossil, 45, 70, 71, 72, 75, 77, 81, 83, 89, 94, 98
Monkey puzzle tree, 63
Monograptids, 33
Moraine, 96
Mososaurs, 55, 87
Mosses, 60
Moths, 84
Murchison, Sir Roderick, 20
Mushrooms, 60
Mussels, 41, 81, 89

Nautiloids, 43–4, 75, 83, 89, 93
Nemertinea, 26
Neuropteris, 62
Newts, 53
Niobrara Limestone, 56
Nummulites, 29, 89, 91, 93

Oaks, 90, 93
Octopus, 41, 43
Oligocene period, 90–2
Oolitic limestone, 83
Operculum, 42
Ordovician period, 71–2
Orogeny, Alpine, 89, 92
    Caledonian, 73
    Hercynian, 78
    Pre-Cambrian, 69
Ossicles, 47

Index

Osteichthyes, 51
Osteolepis, 74
Ostracoderms, 49, 74
Ostracods, 39, 71
Oxen, 98
Oysters, 41, 81, 89

Palaeocene period, 88–90
Palaeolithic man, 98
Palaeoniscids, 77
Palaeotherium, 92
Palaeozoic era, 65, 70 ff.
Palms, 62
Pecopteris, 62
Pecten, 42
Pelycosaurs, 79
Penguins, 93
Pigs, 90
Pines, 63
Pisces, 49
Placoderms, 50
Plants, 57–63
Pleistocene period, 95–9
Plesiosaurs, 54, 81, 84, 87
Pliocene period, 94
Pollen grain study, 99
Polyzoa, 33–4
Porifera, 29–30
Portuguese Man of War, 30
Pre-Cambrian era, 69
Primates, 90
Productids, 75
  spiny, 79
Protozoa, 27–9
Pteridophyta, 61–2
Pterodactyls, 55, 84, 87
Pterygota, 39
Purbeck Marble, 84

Radioactivity, 64

Radiolaria, 27, 29, 70, 93
Raised beaches, 96
Rays, 50, 87
Reefs, 33, 59, 72, 73, 75, 83
Reindeer, 98
Reptiles, classification of, 53–5
  fossil, 79, 81, 82, 84, 89
Reptile eggs, 54
Rhaetic, 82
Rhinoceros, 90, 93, 98
Rhynchonellids, 31, 81, 86
Rhynie Chert, 40
Richthofenia, 79
Rocky Mountains, 86
Rotifera, 26
Rudists, 86
Rugose corals, 32

Sabre-toothed tiger, 93, 95, 98
Salamanders, 53
Sarcodina, 27
Scale trees, 61, 74, 75, 77, 80
Scallops, 41, 91
Scandinavian ice sheet, 96
Scaphopoda, 43
Schizaster, 93
Scorpions, 40, 77
Scyphozoa, 31
Sea cucumbers, *see* Holothuroids, 75
Sea mosses, 30
Seaweed, 70, 72, 73
Sea urchins, *see* Echinoidea, 48, 71,
  72, 75, 81, 84, 86, 89
Seed ferns, 62, 74, 75, 77
Seeds, 62
Sequoia, 63, 95
Serpula, 36
Sharks, 50–1, 74, 75, 77, 79, 84, 87
Sigillaria, 77

Index